Exam Practice

TYPEWRITING SKILLS STAGE II

HEINEMANN
EDUCATIONAL

in association with the RSA Examinations Board

Heinemann Educational,
a division of Heinemann Educational Books Ltd,
Halley Court, Jordan Hill, Oxford OX2 8EJ

OXFORD   LONDON   EDINBURGH
MELBOURNE   SYDNEY   AUCKLAND
IBADAN   NAIROBI   GABORONE   HARARE
KINGSTON   PORTSMOUTH NH (USA)
SINGAPORE   MADRID

First published 1989

British Library Cataloguing in Publication Data
Typewriting skills
Stage II
1. Typing – Manuals
I. Title   II. Series
00,0

ISBN 0-435-45151-0

Produced by DMD, Oxford
Printed by Thompson Litho Ltd, Scotland

Contents

Stationery

In exams you will be handed a folder (Answer Book) containing stationery for your use during the exam.

The letterhead has details of a fictitious organisation, Praxiteles Group, with the address Praxiteles House, Adam Street, London WC2N 6EZ.

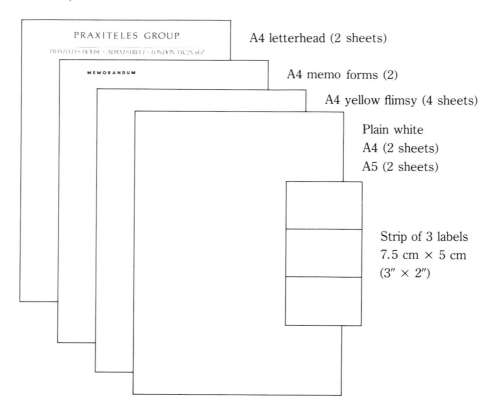

A4 letterhead (2 sheets)

A4 memo forms (2)

A4 yellow flimsy (4 sheets)

Plain white
A4 (2 sheets)
A5 (2 sheets)

Strip of 3 labels
7.5 cm × 5 cm
(3″ × 2″)

In Part 2 exams you will receive plain white paper: 4 sheets A4 and 2 sheets A5, as well as 2 copies of the form for completion.

Introduction

This book provides practice in the types of task included in RSA Stage II Typewriting Skills examinations and the keying-in tasks in Stage II Word Processing examinations. The material has been specially compiled by a group of Chief Examiners currently involved in these examinations.

RSA Examinations Board records its thanks to Margaret Rees-Boughton, Consultant to RSA for Office Subjects, for her work in the origination of the book and in editing it, and to the following Chief Examiners:

Phillip Arnold   Margaret Reid
Alison Knight   and
Carole Machin   Frances Yarham

Checking

Remember: you cannot regard your work as satisfactory until you have checked the text you have typed and corrected any keyboarding errors.

Worked examples are provided after Sections 1–2, and after Sections 3–5, so that you can also check if you have interpreted correctly all of the instructions and the handwriting in each task.

NB: In exams, you must always leave a left margin (at least half-inch). It may not always have been possible to show this in the printed worked examples.

Stationery

The RSA exam letterhead, memo and general forms suitable for use with the exercises in this book are available from bookshops (see previous page). If you should experience any difficulty in buying the Stationery Pad, then contact the Publishers.

RSA Exam Practice

This book is one of a series in which RSA provides practice material based on the types of task set in RSA exams in Typewriting Skills (and the keying-in tasks in Word Processing exams).

In some tasks – especially for Part 2 – the work may be more demanding than that in the exam. This will help you to develop confidence in your ability to cope calmly in the exam with problems that at first sight may *look* forbiddingly complicated.

PRACTICE FOR PART 1 EXAMS

Notes to candidates

Typed drafts for correction

In the exam, there are always handwritten amendments and corrections in these typed drafts. In addition, some of the typed words are ringed round, to call your attention to errors. You must read the surrounding words or sentences to see what is wrong before making all the necessary corrections and amendments in your typed version.

Aim to type, check and correct this type of task within 25 minutes   `25.00`

Letters and memos

In the exam, one or other of these tasks will not be issued until approximately 20 minutes after the starting time. Until then, therefore, you will not know exactly what you will be required to complete during the time allowed (1¼ hours). This is typical of office work; it is rarely possible to issue all work at one time. These handwritten drafts will include words ringed round to call your attention to errors which you must identify and correct.

The draft will include an instruction to take two carbon copies of one of these documents. If you do not produce all the tasks, including the carbon copies, you cannot pass the exam. In addition to correcting all other documents you need to make any necessary corrections to your own typing in the carbon copies so that they are accurate.

There will also be instructions to type two labels. If one of these is requested for a document with a special mark, eg URGENT, this special mark must also be typed on the label.

There will be only three labels in the stationery pack, so you must try to complete the typing of one of them at your first attempt. If you totally spoil available stationery, you should re-type the proper details on a plain piece of paper.

Aim to type, check and correct a letter, memo, carbon copies and labels within 40 minutes   `40.00`

1 Typed drafts for correction

Task 1.1

WHICH MORTGAGE REPAYMENT METHOD? ← *(spaced caps)*

A BRIEF GUIDE ← *(leave 2 clear line spaces)*

Buying a house is likely to be the biggest financial commitment ever most people make in their lives. The majority of homes are bought with the help of a mortgage. There are ~~several methods~~ of ✓ repaying a mortgage and each has its own merits. ~~Whichever mortgage you choose, life assurance cover will be required.~~

THE OPTIONS

1 With a repayment mortgage a single monthly payment is made of interest due for the month plus (plus) an amount of the capital outstanding. By using this repayment method the loan is repaid at the end of the mortgage term. However, no surplus (iss) left for the borrower.   *(double line spacing)*

2 The endowment mortgage has become very popular in recent years. Under this scheme interest only is paid. A further payment is made, normally monthly, to a life assurance company() This extra payment gives life cover and builds up a capital sum which repays the mortgage at the end of its term. *There are various types of endowment policy.* ~~Several kinds of endowment policy are available.~~ These range from low start, low cost plans to full 'with profits' plans.

3 A pension plan mortgage works in much the same way as an endowment mortgage. Interest only is paid. Instead of the loan being repaid with the aid of a life assurance policy, the lump sum from a pension contract is used. This type of contract can be taken out by the self-employed and those who are employed but are not in a pension scheme. It can also be used by (employer's) choosing to opt out of their (employees) pension scheme. ~~To people who qualify, this type of mortgage can be~~

4 A unit linked mortgage scheme also works in a similar way to an endowment mortgage. The capital sum to repay the loan at the end of the term is built up by payments to a unit trust fund ~~with~~ an insurance company.   *(recy)*
   thro'

3

TRAVELLING ABROAD ← *spaced caps* *leave 3 clear line spaces*

<u>PAYING YOUR WAY</u>

Wherever you are going, you are likely to need some foreign ~~amount~~. ~~You should remember~~ *do not forget* that some countries have a limit on the ~~currency~~ of foreign currency you are allowed to take into and out of the country. Order at least 5 working days before ~~you leave~~ *departure*. ✓

No matter how far you are planning to travel, Europe or further afield, it is recommended that you take a supply of travellers cheques. For most countries it is advisable ~~to~~ to take cheques in the currency of your destination. You are likely to get a better rate of exchange. Any unused cheques can be kept for your next trip or sold back to the bank. *suff*

Eurocheque is a convenient way of making payments abroad if you are going to Europe or the Mediterranean. Together with a Eurocheque card you can use them just as you use your normal cheques at home. ~~For paying bills, for buying goods and services and for getting cash from a bank.~~ Eurocheques can be cashed at over 200,000 banks and used at over 5 million shops, restaurants and hotels showing the EC sign. They are each guaranteed for up to the local equivalent of £100.

Of course major credit cards are now being increasingly~~ly~~ accepted world wide. *double line spacing*

<u>SAFEGUARDS</u>

A Never leave cash or valuables in a car or hotel room. *Keep your credit cards in a sep place.* ~~Avoid leaving your plastic cards loose.~~

B Always check the rates of exchange offered by hotels or shops. It may well be worth waiting for the banks to open ~~in the morning~~.

C Always keep a record of your Eurocheque and travellers cheque transactions.

D Always make sure you have access to extra money for emergencies.

E Always be prepared to provide some proof of identity (ideally your passport) when cashing travellers cheques and Eurocheques.

F Always take a copy of your travel insurance policy with you.

Typist: 1st & last paras in double - rest in single

PRAXI GAS COOKERS — _spaced caps_

SERIES TWO

PLAN 6 SBS

Have you ever thought how much you enjoy being in the kitchen? No
longer is it a place of hard work; today's kitchen is bright, well
thought out and a real pleasure in which to create and live.

3 clear lines here — _that we have def improved the design_

You will be pleased to know ~~that we have been improving the
design~~ of our cookers because we view the kitchen as your
own "control centre" as well as a place to enjoy. We can
offer you:

1 easy controls;

2 the ease of gas;

3 cookers built into your present kitchen;

   the mfrs
4 five year cover from ~~the supplier~~;

5 good working height for comfort.

We offer you the very best design, the most responsive fuel and a
~~complete system~~. ~~This adds up to a full cooking system because~~
~~comprehensive range.~~ we offer cookers, ovens, hobs, grills, micowaves and hoods. All
our products can be built in or free standing.

You will find enough styles in warm brown or white to blend in with
your kitchen, whether it is in a flat or a country mansion.

Our range takes in all the new trends but it also meets the demands
of the versatile cook. At the same time, it fits in with the needs
of busy working people with no spare time.

Should you have trouble in finding any of our products, please
contact _your nearest_ Praxi branch. Our aim is always to develop and improve.
Whilst our leaflet is correct at the time of printing, some feat-
tures may be changed because we need to put safety first and
foremost. ~~We cannot stress the dangers too much.~~

If you require cookery advice please write to The Home Economist,
Praxi Gas Appliances, Adam Street, London, WC2N 6EZ. We also have
a "Users' Club" and a magazine is published three times a year
containing views, hints, recipes, etc; new users receive their
first issue free ~~but there is a small charge for later issues.~~

ON THE ROAD ← *spaced caps*

The cost of motoring is high enough these days without paying too much for your insurance. We can offer you a range of competitively priced insurances for cars and motor cycles. Our 600 local agents are able to provide friendly, helpful advice. They can also assist you in the event of a claim. Few insurance ~~organisations~~ cos can match Praxi's use of technology combined with the very real personal service offered to you.

COVER FOR YOUR CAR ← *3 clear line spaces*

Our comprehensive car insurance policy has a wide range of extras *double line spacing* including cover for the following:

1 Wind screen damage to and unlimited amount without affecting your no claim discount

2 Personal effects up to £250

3 Medical expenses up to £250 per person

4 Legal defence costs to an unlimited amount

5 Personal accident benefits up to £5,000 for you and/or your spouse for death and certain disabilities.

There are discounts of up to 65% and a "protected discount" option for drivers with maximum no no claim discount. For most policyholders not normally entitled to a no claim discount there is a 25% ~~introductory saving~~ *special reduction*. Further savings can be made if you ~~choose to~~ restrict driving to your spouse and yourself or if you choose a voluntary excess.

MOTOR CYCLE INSURANCE

As a motor cyclist you need the best protection. Our motor cycle policy gives you the kind of cover you need on the road at the right price.

As well as loss of or damage
~~If you lose or any harm is done~~ to your motor cycle, you are covered for liability to other people and for legal defence costs to an extended amount. In addition, we offer a generous no claim discount of up to 35%. Cover is normally limited to the policyholder *altho'* it can be unlimited to include other named riders.

~~The insurance operates anywhere in the UK and applications for use abroad may be considered for short periods.~~

6

PRAXI FINANCIAL SERVICES

TODAY'S WOMAN AND FINANCE ~(spaced caps)~

WE CAN HELP YOU

[Typist note: 1st & last paras in double linespacing – rest in single please.]

Today's woman is a wizard of high finance and not the fragile creature of 50 years ago. At Praxi Financial Services we want to <u>know</u> just how today's woman copes with the challenge she has set herself

Society at last realises that women are helping to balance the economy because:

1   they represent 46 per cent of the labour market

2   they will take up 80 per cent of the new jobs from 1995 onwards

3   they often have no alternative but to be ~~the household's~~ *resp for the household's money*

4 women will have government backing to manage ~thier~ own affairs.

✓ We are ~~carrying out~~ *conducting a* survey throughout the British Isles to find out just what the attitude of women is to money, and <u>what</u> else we can do to help women to manage their financial affairs ~well.~

At Praxi, *our new finance cttee* ~~have set up a new advisory body which~~ consists of successful women. It will be chaired by an ex National Hunt champion who is also chairman of a development corporation *and* its members also include an actress and a BBC presenter.

We are firmly convinced that women every where have the right to be *aware of* financial matters, and should be able to handle their own affairs by themselves.

We hope that you can spare some of your precious time to give a hand with our survey. We will then (*a complete picture*) be able to build up of the modern woman and her financial management. You will also be able to support some favourite charities at the same time because we will donate 10p for every survey sent back to us. It will cost you nothing ~~to complete the survey because no stamp is needed.~~

(Leave 5 clear line spaces here)

Please return it to Praxi Financial Services, 8 John Adam Street, London, WC2N 6EZ ~~no later than the end of the month~~ in the special envelope included in your magazine.

PRAXI CHILD PLAN ← spaced caps   leave 3 clear line spaces

1   Up to £15,000 or more for your child at 21

2   Life cover   Immed

3   Your payments kept up free if illness or accident
    stops you working

4   The cash sum fully protected if you die

Introducing a simple, secure way of giving your child a
~~serious start~~ vital headstart in adult life. The Praxi Child Plan could provide   double line spacing
your son or daughter with a substantial cash sum when they are 21.
It is easy to arrange and because you choose how much you want to
invest each month, it is tailored to suit you.

A helping hand from just 30p a day

For as little as 30p a day
~~For the tiny sum of £2.10 per week~~, you can look forward to providing
real financial help to your son or daughter at a time when it will be
so useful. This help could enable your child to carry on studying
for a qualification ~~rather than having to accept the first job that
comes along~~ or perhaps assist with the ~~cost~~ exp of setting up a home.

Life cover

The Praxi Child Plan has life (life) insurance built in. If you should
die before the end of the plan, the life insurance benefit would be paid
out right away. All monthly payments would be continued until the end
of the plan. Your investment would not be affected and the cash
sum would be paid in the normal way. If serious illness or accident
kept you off work for six months or more, all subsequent monthly
payments would be paid for you until you were well enough to work.

A Praxi Child Plan makes sense for every parent with a child now
aged 11 or under. The (soooner) you start ~~your Praxi Child Plan~~, the
greater will be the cash payout. Just think of the rewards you will
reap when your child is 21.

PRAXI LONDON WEEKENDS

Everybody loves to visit London and its shops, buildings, art
treasures, (sports and entertainment) mean fun for all. ~~You will~~
~~never tire of visiting~~ famous places of interest.

Praxi hotels can help you to get more out of your week-end by
giving you value for money and taking the hard work off your
hands.

Leave 3 lines clear

SIGHTSEEING

enjoy a exp on your trip to London you will see more on

With so much to ~~see in London you will see more on~~ an organised
tour. Look at the savings we have been able to make on our
special luxury tours.

    1 Coaches will give you a panoramic tour of London with trips (to)
       to Kew Gardens and Hampton Court.

    2 Boat cruises show you the riverside from Westminster to
       Greenwich.

    3 Take a <u>trip on</u> a London bus – either a "hop on hop off" trip
       or a (continous) journey.

    4 Take our special shopping tour with lunch included in the price.

FREE DISCOUNT VOUCHERS – (Spaced Caps)

✓ Make the most of the sights of London with our ~~book of~~ *vouchers* free
discount vouchers to London's favourite places. At a much
reduced cost you can visit the *London* Zoo, the Planetarium and Madame
Tussaud's. (if) you want to tread on the hallowed turf of Wembley
now is your chance, and instead of being filled with horror at the
price, *we can recom the* ~~visit the~~ horrors of the Tower at our expense.

At the end of a busy day you will want to come back to comfort
and good food. Praxi hotels offer comfortable rooms with
tea/coffee making facilities, television and private bathroom.
Children under 14 receive free accommodation if they share.
Adult guests may dine in the superb surroundings of our smart
dining rooms and a full English breakfast is included for
the price paid.

If you wish to see a show or visit a nightspot, please note this
on your booking form. ~~We will arrange this through our booking agent.~~

*Typist: 1st a last paras
need to be in double
spacing*

Task 2.1 – letter

Take one carbon copy on yellow paper and another on plain white paper for Eileen Joyce. Address a label to Betterprint Ltd and another to Miss Joyce.

Our ref BF/md3

The Manager
Betterprint Ltd
69 Blueford Lane
LONDON
SE21 5PP

Dear Sir

PRAXITELES HOUSE STATIONERY

I am pleased to ack your recent letter. It will without doubt be necy for us to meet in order to discuss the final look of our new logo. To this end I suggest Fri type the date for Friday of next week at 10 o'clock. If this is incon please contact my assistant, Eileen Joyce, who will arrange a further date and time.

the headed paper of all
We now have it in mind to bring / our other cos into line with our own new stationery. However, we must ensure that there is absolutely no confusion caused, by having logos that are too alike. people do not get the various companies mixed up

It will be vital to ensure that they can be linked but not confused. I suggest that we also discuss this points at our meeting. Perhaps you could then get your artwork work people to start asap on the new designs.

I must congratulate you and yr staff on having made such very swift progress on this job coming up with the good's so quickly. I look forward to our meeting.

Yours faithfully
PRAXITELES HOUSE LTD

Bryan Ferrara
Marketing Manager

(Memorandum)

From   Bryan Ferrara

To   Eileen Joyce

Ref   BF/md3

<u>Urgent</u>

NEW LOGOS FOR HEADED PAPER

You wl find enclosed a copy of a letter ~~have~~ sent today to the Manager of B———L——.
Please note that I have asked him to contact you shd the date I have suggested for the meeting not be (convienient.)

Over the next two weeks, I am unavailable on 3 days. These are Tues of next week and Mon and Weds of the week after.

Can you please arrange an in-house meeting ~~members of staff in the Marketing Department of Poaritelar House~~ prior to the above meeting ↑to get a full picture of any points that staff wish to raise. Wd next Monday at either 10 am or 1400 hours be possible?   (So that the opp is taken)

I have recd your report on the new advertising campaign. I agree that the new logo should be used and that the advert should go out at prime time if we are to get a good public response. [Can you please get to work on this ~~state~~ ~~these sorts of times~~ are taken up very swiftly.   (as I believe that these slots)

11

Please type this memorandum. Take one carbon copy on yellow paper and one on plain white paper for our Managing Director. Kindly type a label to be addressed to Ms Linda Wade Promotions Co-ordinator. Thank you.

Ref DH/A142

From David Hadfield
        Sales Manager

To   Ms Linda Wade
        Promotions Co-ordinator

SALES   INFORMATION   PACKAGE

At our recent departmental cttee meeting ~~marketing co-ordination seminar~~ it was resolved that we should completely redesign our literature.

Therefore a few days ago I sent you a proposed price list. However, it was only a draft copy and we now need to make some minor amendments.

Please notice that the charge for ~~Kindly note the cost of~~ printing the same logo on both back and front of a sweatshirt has had to be increased. An extra £0.85 per garment will be added to the appropriate cost. Also the price for each additional print colour will be 90p. Kindly emphasise that once we have received an order ~~for sweatshirts and teeshirts~~ we can gntee delivery of clothing within four weeks.

In addition the children's range of sweatshirts will be extended. Sizes CT1 (22" chest) and CT2 (24 in chest) is available forthwith.

At the meeting the Managing Director suggested that we should send clients small samples of material to demonstrate the superb quality of our fabric. Another advantage is that each swatch wd show the range of colours we have available. This certainly seems to be a good idea as customers are often confused about the blue colours we offer. I therefore enclose an example of the type of booklet we propose.

Please let me have an estimate of costs along with yr views. I must rec yr opinions immed as prompt action needs taking about the feasibility of this plan.

Please type this letter and address a label.

Our Ref DH/Q963
Your Ref SM/ts

URGENT

Mrs S Moore
42 Anton St
WIMBORNE
Dorset
BH21 7HL

Dear Mrs Moore

QUOTATION FOR SWEATSHIRTS

Thank you for your recent correspondence enquiring about
the cost of sweatshirts printed w your (clubs) logo. // We
confirm that / we wd charge £9.50 per garment. The
for a minimum quantity of 50 shirts
enclosed cat has full info about our pricing strategy.
These charges are inclusive of all artwork, stencil and
set-up costs. Please note that delivery wl be within
... weeks from rec of your order.
(See memo)

We are currently offering a 10% reduction on ~~leisure~~
~~garments, such as teeshirts and~~ sweatshirts. To qualify,
your order shd be recd by us before please date for
two weeks today.

We look forward to hearing from you.

Yrs scly
PRAXIPRINT CLOTHING

David Hadfield
Sales Manager

Memorandum — take one carbon copy on yellow paper and one on white paper for David Martin.

Ref HK/ccc

To Sharon Sinclair, A/cs   From Henry Kanta, Director

Priority

CHILDLINE CHARITY CONCERT

The final arrangements are now in preparation for this concert to be held on Tues (Put the date of the Tuesday of next week). Various members of the organising cttee will be asking you to authorise payments ~~and to provide funds for expenses~~ over the next few days. If you have any (queries) about any of these, this must now be treated as urgent. (please contact me immed, as)

[You may rec calls from the agents who (represents) the stars who are top of the bill. They are, of course, giving their services free. They wl expect their exps to be met. The two groups, /whose agents are likely to contact you are Bitter Harvest and Tricycle Clips. There may also be enquiries from the agents of these 3 artists about costs — Rory Galbraith, (Tanya Chitraj) and (Bird Coltrane). If you need any more info concerning these, please contact me.]

Do not authorise any payments less than £50 or over two thousand pounds. I will leave it to yr judgment as to whether the payment required seems fair. Consider the status of the artist or artists whose agent makes the claim.

I enclose a ~~complete rundown of stars on the bill~~ full list of artists giving their services for this event. If we have any (cancelations), replacements or additional acts, I sh let you know at once.

Address one label for this letter for posting
and another to Martin Black
Concert Organiser

Our ref HK/AA/CCC

Mr A Amir
Agency Manager
Acme Acts
North Hill
LONDON
NW57 7LH

Dear Mr Amir

TRICYCLE CLIPS — CHI _____ CHA _____ CO _____

This is to confirm that all expenses ~~incurred in connection with this concert~~ will be paid for the group's appearance at the Childline Benefit. Please pass on our deepest thanks to them for offering their services free. I have no doubt that they will be a very big draw, wh will ensure as much money as poss being raised for Childline. // Polygon Records hope to record the concert. They are prepared to donate all profits. Please wd you let me know if the group is prepared to release any royalties from the record to Childline. Will their current record company allow them temp release from contract ~~almost continually degrade~~ on the Hexagon label? for the recording to come out

Complimentary tickets for yourself and nine guests are enclosed.

Yrs sncly
PRAXITELES PROMOTIONS

Henry Kanta
Director

Please type this letter taking one carbon copy on yellow paper and one on plain white paper for Mr Strong. Two labels are required – one to Mr Harrison and one to Mr Strong. Thank you.

Our Ref PC/Store

URGENT

Mr T R Harrison
Renting Manager
Prospect Commercial
14 Ramsey Rd
READING RG7 4AF

Dr Mr Harrison

STORAGE AT RACEDOWN FARM

Following our recent visit and telephone conversation w you, we are now able to state our exact storage requirements. We shd like to rent the sheds for a period of four months starting on Fri (insert date for next week). The farmer concerned has very kindly agreed to unload and load the lorries so we will pay a £2 handling charge per pallet. These exps will be payable to Mr Strong upon rec of his invoice. We sh try to give 2 (day's) notice of any movement into or out of the building.

We are sending a copy of this letter to Mr M Strong↑ for info purposes. (at Racedown Farm, Oakley, Basingstoke, RG23 7XT)

The draft lease is enclosed. Please note that the only minor alteration we require (concern) the section about insurance. We trust that this amendment will be in order. [Please can you send us the appropriate paperwork ready for sig so that we can complete the nec documentation. It is vital that this is undertaken asap since we wish to deliver the first load next week.

We look forward to hearing from you.

Yours sincerely
PRAXITELES GROUP

Peter Connolly
Warehouse Manager

Task 2.8 – memo

Typist – please type this memorandum.

To Trevor Benham

From   Peter Connolly   Ref PC/Store/RF

RACEDOWN   FARM   NEAR   BASINGSTOKE

You wl be pleased to hear that ~~To relieve our warehouse overcrowding problem~~ I have arranged temp storage facilities at the above address.

Mr Strong has ~~kindly~~ agreed to handle the pallets wh means we shall not need to take our forklift to the farm.

(See letter)

As we shall be paying a £.? charge per pallet to the farmer, we must keep an accurate record of the actual number of items involved. ~~I therefore suggest that each lorry driver gives a copy of the load sheet to Mr Strong.~~ Please ensure this is organised satisfactorily.

I confirm that one shed is 260 square metres while the other is slightly smaller at 163 sq m. [I hope we can start delivering to the (sight) next week. However, we need to complete the hus documentation

before we begin using the two sheds.

I shall send you further data including the (telephone number full address,) etc, when appropriate.

Address two labels – one to Ms Galsworthy and the other for her to return to me at Praxiteles House.* – MF

Our Ref MF/IC34

CONFIDENTIAL

Ms Diane Galsworthy
Larch Way
FERNDOWN
Dorset
BH44 6HY

Dear Ms Galsworthy

PRAXI SUPREMA ICE CREAM MAKER

Thank you for your letter w copy for the Praxi Suprema Info Book. Your draft wording is just what we were looking for. It is very clear and concise and should make the working of our new machine ~~not only straightforward and totally uncomplicated but also an enjoyable experience that~~ simple for users. I wd, however, recom that we make the following changes ~~in order~~ so that there is no ambiguity.

In the section headed "Making ice cream" change the word's "should be well mixed" to "must be well amalgamated". // In the section headed "Cleaning" change "inner surface" to "protective coating". // In the section headed "Safety in the home" change "on any hot surface" to "on or near any source of heat".

// I cannot see that any further changes will be necy to your copy. If you agree these, the ~~book~~ booklet can go to print by type the date of Monday of the week after next here.

Your original draft is enclosed for alteration. Please contact my sec, Elmer Dodd, if you have any queries.

Yrs sncly
PRAXI HOUSEWARES PLC

Marcus Finkelstein

---

* See details of RSA exam stationery at front of this book.

Take one carbon copy of this memorandum on yellow paper and one on plain white paper for Sales Promotions.

Ref: MF/IC35
To: Mary Josephs
From: Marcus Finkelstein

P_____ S _____ ICE CREAM MAKER

I have today rec'd copy for the instruction book for this new machine from Ms Diane Galsworthy. Apart from a few minor changes ~~which you will see I have in detail below~~ this (seem) just what we wanted. I sh ask her to agree to these changes, and we shd then be ready to go to print.

Please can you confirm that ~~all the recipes together instruction books~~ copy for the Recipe Guide is also ready? The two can then go together and have the same cover illustration.

I suggest that we ask the printers to go for a size of approx 5" wide by eight inches deep.

to check thro' all the other arrangements
I must arrange to see you in connection with the launch. Wl either next Wed at ten in the morning or 3pm be a convenient appt for you?

The actual launch date has not yet been made final. Would you let me know when you would be unable to attend? Many thanks for your help. We could not have managed to get these booklets ready without your hard work.

of any date during the next two months

Take 2 carbon copies – 1 on yellow paper + the other on plain white for Ms Phillips. Type a label to Mr Leslie, + address the other to Mr Nix at Praxiteles Group* for Mr Leslie's reply.

Our ref CN/H27C

CONFIDENTIAL

Mr D Leslie
Abbass House
WESTCLIFF-ON-SEA Essex SSO 4AX

Dear Mr Leslie

<u>Court Appearance for Speeding Offence</u>

We have now had the opp to look thro' yr statement in relation to the charge of speeding on the Andover to Salisbury road. There is clear evidence that you were travelling at 20 miles per hour above the (relevent) limit! It wd appear that you wl have to plead guilty to the offence of exceeding the speed limit.

~~We have checked the police procedures which are in order.~~ We wd like to rec details of the approx mileage you travel annually. Please also supply any other details wh you bel may be useful. For instance, you shd say if you could lose yr job if your licence was taken away for any period of time.

Subject to any endorsements already on yr licence, you may be ~~given any endorsement~~ given three penalty points + also be fined. However, if you have committed 2 or more (offence) then you may lose yr licence. We sh

20

obviously need to have full details of yr motoring record. [The case] [will be heard in Andover Magistrates' Court. This] is listed for Wednesday [give date for Wed of week after next] at 10 am. The above info. is therefore needed urgently & we enclose an addressed label for yr reply.

Yrs sely
PRAXITELES GROUP

Christopher Nix
Solicitor

(Memo) to Davina Phillips   Ref CN/427C   From Christopher Nix

Please ~~undertake the following appointment~~ make an urgent diary note to attend the court hearing for Mr Leslie. I attach a copy of the letter so that you can extract details of (date, time & place) (which I have today sent to him)

I appreciate that the case will be heard in ------- Magistrates' Court & this will mean you have to travel by train.

(However, the case is listed for 10 am. It may be possible for you to return to London by 1400 hrs to avoid the loss of the whole (days') work. The firm will, of course, pay yr exps in full. // Once I have all the data I shall give you the file // Mr Leslie will be pleading guilty to the charge but I ~~definitely~~ still think ~~feel~~ we need to discuss the matter. Please contact my sec to arrange a time for this.

(Memorandum)

To Jason Markham   From Elaine Griffiths
Ref EG/CD7

CLASSICAL COMPACT DISC COMPETITION WINNERS

The results of the above competition have now been decided and are as follows.

The first prize of the complete set of Wagner's "Ring" cycle has been (awarded) to Malcolm Beardshaw. The second prize of 2 Mozart operas goes to Jane Handley. The third prize of the four Brahms symphonies goes to Mary Bradley. You wl find details of the winners' home addresses and telephone numbers on the attached copy letter sent to them today. All (prize's) are ~~releases~~ ~~that are on sale at full price in the shops and are~~ from the Polygon cat of recordings. [Presentation of the prizes will be in the Romney cttee room. on Wed (Put Wednesday of next week's date) at 10 am

Please wd you arrange for the usual refreshments – ~~coffee~~, biscuits etc – to be laid on and served by nine thirty. Please also arrange for all staff who need to be present / ~~the other staff in the company~~ to be informed of the date, time and venue immed. I shd contact them in person – there is no need to put it in writing. [A representative from Polygon Records will present the prizes and we also hope to have Sir James Priddy, the conductor, w us on the day. As this has yet to be confirmed, make a provisional booking for him at the presentation. As you know, each set of compact discs will be a signed (editions.) Please check the sigs on each set before they are wrapped.

Take one carbon copy on yellow paper and another on white paper for Jason Markham. Address a label for the letter and a second label to Cathy Hands, Publicity. Make all the changes shown

Our ref EG/CD4
Your ref PR63/SJP

PERSONAL

Mr Tom Perry
Classics Manager
Polygon Records
BIRMINGHAM
B97 4PQ

Dr Mr Perry

COMPACT DISC PRESENTATIONS

Details of the ~~names and addresses of all three~~ winners of the compact disc competition are on the enclosed copy letter. The presentation ~~will be held next week~~ is scheduled for 10 am next Wednesday and will be in the R_____ c_____ r___ in Praxiteles House.

This letter is to confirm that we sh pay yr exps in full, and also those for Sir James, if he is able to attend. Please would you let me know by Tuesday night. I will then get my sec to make the necy reservations. *return if either of you will require overnight accom on*

I look forward to seeing you next week. Please let me know at once if there is any further information you require.
Yours sincerely
PRAXITELES PROMOTIONS
Harriet Foot
Director

Task 2.15 – letter

Take a carbon copy on yellow paper + one on plain white for Miss Ryde. A label is required addressed to Mr Brook

Our ref ST/LC/C48

Mr P Brook
Personnel Manager
Astra Associates
110 Elm St
BASINGSTOKE   RG23 9RW

Dr Mr Brook

FRENCH FOR BUSINESS AND PLEASURE

Thank you for yr recent enquiry about our short courses. // We firmly bel that the language skills of the workforce in Britian may well be the decisive factor when competing in Europe. We are sure it wl be necy to be able to speak + understand at least one major foreign language.

In the introductory unit we ~~give much attention to~~ spend most time on spoken communication. By the end of the course we expect students to be able to entertain + welcome foreign people. They shd also be able to exchange simple info about themselves + their firm.

Miss Ryde, who is a language specialist, will contact yr org to discuss the matter further. She wl make an appt with yr Marketing Manager, Mr Dalton, within the next few days. In the meantime, we confirm that we could run a French course starting at 6.15 pm + finishing at 1945 hrs.

Please contact us again if you require any further details. At Praxiteles we aim to provide the very best language training.

Yours scly
PRAXITELES GROUP

(Mrs) Simone Thomas
EUROPEAN LANGUAGES SECTION

Memo to Miss J Ryde

(Please address a label to her at Court House)

From S Thomas

Ref ST/C4   URGENT

Short Courses in French

I know you wl be pleased to read the enclosed letter from one of our clients, Cox (UK) PLC of ~~Woking Industrial Estate, Unit 11, Chalswood Rd~~ Woking. It is an excellent ref for the course. I like the Managing (Directors) comment that even he coped! As you can see, they wd now like us to timetable a second course on Mondays, starting on (give date for the Monday of the week after next). You will note ~~the class~~ size wl have to be increased from 12 f/t (employee) to fourteen. Please contact them asap to discuss the matter.

Please also contact Mr -----, who is the Marketing Manager of a firm called Astra Associates in Basingstoke.

I enclose a copy of the letter I have written to them & sh be pleased if you wl ~~treat~~ the matter as urgent. ~~since they are very keen to run a course asap.~~

delighted with the way
You must be ~~really pleased by the progress~~ your department is developing. The monthly reports are very encouraging.

(The number is Basingstoke 3878272.)

Worked examples

1 Typed drafts for correction

W H I C H   M O R T G A G E   R E P A Y M E N T   M E T H O D ?

A BRIEF GUIDE

Buying a house is likely to be the biggest financial commitment most people ever make in their lives. The majority of homes are bought with the help of a mortgage. There are several methods of repaying a mortgage and each has its own merits.

THE OPTIONS

1   With a repayment mortgage a single monthly payment is made

    of interest due for the month plus an amount of the capital

    outstanding. By using this repayment method the loan is

    repaid at the end of the mortgage term. However, no

    surplus is left for the borrower.

2   The endowment mortgage has become very popular in recent years. Under this scheme interest only is paid. A further payment is made, normally monthly, to a life assurance company. This extra payment gives life cover and builds up a capital sum which repays the mortgage at the end of its term. There are various types of endowment policy. These range from low start, low cost plans to full 'with profits' plans.

3   A pension plan mortgage works in much the same way as an endowment mortgage. Interest only is paid. Instead of the loan being repaid with the aid of a life assurance policy, the lump sum from a pension contract is used. This type of contract can be taken out by the self-employed and those who are employed but are not in a pension scheme. It can also be used by employees choosing to opt out of their employer's pension scheme.

4   A unit linked mortgage scheme also works in a similar way to an endowment mortgage. The capital sum necessary to repay the loan at the end of the term is built up by payments to a unit trust fund through an insurance company.

T R A V E L L I N G   A B R O A D

PAYING YOUR WAY

Wherever you are going, you are likely to need some foreign currency. Do not forget that some countries have a limit on the amount of foreign currency you are allowed to take into and out of the country. Order at least 5 working days before you leave.

No matter how far you are planning to travel, Europe or further afield, it is recommended that you take a sufficient supply of travellers cheques. For most countries it is advisable to take cheques in the currency of your destination. You are likely to get a better rate of exchange. Any unused cheques can be kept for your next trip or sold back to the bank.

Eurocheque is a convenient way of making payments abroad if you are going to Europe or the Mediterranean. Together with a Eurocheque card you can use them just as you use your normal cheques at home. Eurocheques can be cashed at over 200,000 banks and used at over 5 million shops, restaurants and hotels showing the EC sign. They are each guaranteed for up to the local equivalent of £100.

Of course major credit cards are now being increasingly accepted

worldwide.

SAFEGUARDS

A   Never leave cash or valuables in a car or hotel room. Keep your credit cards in a separate place.

B   Always check the rates of exchange offered by hotels or shops. It may well be worth waiting for the banks to open.

C   Always keep a record of your travellers cheque and Eurocheque transactions.

D   Always make sure you have access to extra money for emergencies.

E   Always be prepared to provide some proof of identity (ideally your passport) when cashing travellers cheques and Eurocheques.

F   Always take a copy of your travel insurance policy with you.

Task 1.3

PRAXI   GAS   COOKERS

SERIES TWO

PLAN 6 SBS

Have you ever thought how much you enjoy being in the kitchen? No
longer is it a place of hard work; today's kitchen is bright, well
thought out and a real pleasure in which to create and live.

You will be pleased to know that we have definitely improved the
design of our cookers because we view the kitchen as your
own "control centre" as well as a place to enjoy. We can
offer you:

   1 easy controls;

   2 the ease of gas;

   3 cookers built into your present kitchen;

   4 five year cover from the manufacturers;

   5 good working height for comfort.

We offer you the very best design, the most responsive fuel and a complete system. We offer cookers, ovens, hobs, grills, microwaves and
hoods. All our products can be built in or free standing.

Our range takes in all the new trends but it also meets the demands
of the versatile cook. At the same time, it fits in with the needs
of busy working people with no spare time.

You will find enough styles in white or warm brown to blend in with
your kitchen, whether it is in a flat or a country mansion.

Should you have trouble in finding any of our products, please
contact your nearest Praxi branch. Our aim is always to develop
and improve. Whilst our leaflet is correct at the time of printing,
some features may be changed because we need to put safety first
and foremost.

If you require cookery advice please write to The Home Economist,
Praxi Gas Appliances, Adam Street, London, WC2N 6EZ. We also have
a "Users' Club" and a magazine is published three times a year
containing views, hints, recipes, etc; new users receive their
first issue free.

Task 1.4

ON   THE   ROAD

The cost of motoring is high enough these days without paying too
much for your insurance. We can offer you a range of competitively
priced insurances for cars and motor cycles. Our 600 local agents
are able to provide friendly, helpful advice. They can also assist
you in the event of a claim. Few insurance companies can match
Praxi's use of technology combined with the very real personal
service offered to you.

COVER FOR YOUR CAR

Our comprehensive car insurance policy has a wide range of extras

including cover for the following:

   1 Windscreen damage to an unlimited amount without
      affecting your no claim discount

   2 Personal effects up to £250

   3 Medical expenses up to £250 per person

   4 Legal defence costs to an unlimited amount

   5 Personal accident benefits up to £5,000 for you
      and/or your spouse for death and certain disabilities.

There are discounts of up to 65% and a "protected discount" option
for drivers with maximum no claim discount. For most policyholders
not normally entitled to a no claim discount there is a 25%
introductory saving. Further savings can be made if you restrict
driving to yourself and your spouse or if you choose a voluntary
excess.

MOTOR CYCLE INSURANCE

As a motor cyclist you need the best protection. Our motor cycle
policy gives you the kind of cover you need on the road at the right
price.

As well as loss of or damage to your motor cycle, you are covered
for liability to other people and for legal defence costs to an unlimited
amount. In addition, we offer a generous no claim discount of up to
35%. Cover is normally limited to the policyholder although it can be
extended to include other named riders.

Task 1.5

PRAXI FINANCIAL SERVICES

T O D A Y ' S   W O M A N   A N D   F I N A N C E

WE CAN HELP YOU

Today's woman is a wizard of high finance and not the fragile creature
of 50 years ago. At Praxi Financial Services we want to know just how
today's woman copes with the challenge she has set herself.

Society at last realises that women are helping to balance the ecomomy
because:

1 they represent 46 per cent of the labour market

2 they will take up 80 per cent of the new jobs from 1995 onwards

3 they often have no alternative but to be responsible for the
   household's money

4 women will have government backing to manage their own affairs.

We are firmly convinced that women everywhere have the right to be aware of
financial matters, and should be able to handle their own affairs by
themselves.

At Praxi, our new finance committee consists of successful women. It
will be chaired by an ex National Hunt champion who is also chairman
of a development corporation and its members also include an actress and
a BBC presenter.

We are carrying out a survey throughout the British Isles to find out
just what the attitude of women is to money, and what else we can do
to help women to manage their financial affairs well.

We hope that you can spare some of your precious time to give a hand
with our survey. We will then be able to build up a complete picture
of the modern woman and her financial management. You will also be
able to support some favourite charities at the same time because we
will donate 10p for every survey sent back to us. It will cost you
nothing.

Please return it to Praxi Financial Services, 8 John Adam Street,

London, WC2N 6EZ in the special envelope included in your magazine.

Task 1.6

P R A X I   C H I L D   P L A N

1 Up to £15,000 or more for your child at 21

2 Immediate life cover

3 The cash sum fully protected if you die

4 Your payments kept up free if illness or accident
   stops you working

Introducing a simple, secure way of giving your child a vital

headstart in adult life. The Praxi Child Plan could provide

your son or daughter with a substantial cash sum when they are 21.

It is easy to arrange and because you choose how much you want to

invest each month, it is tailored to suit you.

A helping hand from just 30p a day

For as little as 30p a day, you can look forward to providing
real financial help to your son or daughter at a time when it will
be so useful. This help could enable your child to carry on studying
for a qualification or perhaps assist with the expense of setting
up a home.

Life cover

The Praxi Child Plan has life insurance built in. If you should
die before the end of the plan, the life insurance benefit would be
paid out right away. All monthly payments would be continued until
the end of the plan. Your investment would not be affected and the
cash sum would be paid in the normal way. If accident or serious
illness kept you off work for six months or more, all subsequent
monthly payments would be paid for you until you were well enough
to work.

A Praxi Child Plan makes sense for every parent with a child now
aged 11 or under. The sooner you start, the greater will be the
cash payout. Just think of the rewards you will reap when your child
is 21.

PRAXI LONDON WEEKENDS

Everybody loves to visit London and its shops, buildings, art

treasures, entertainment and sports mean fun for all.

Praxi hotels can help you to get more out of your weekend by giving you
value for money and taking the hard work off your hands.

SIGHTSEEING

With so much to enjoy and experience on your trip to London you
will see more on an organised tour. Look at the savings we have
been able to make on our special luxury tours.

1   Coaches will give you a panoramic tour of London with
    trips to Kew Gardens and Hampton Court.

2   Boat cruises show you the riverside from Westminster to
    Greenwich.

3   Take a trip on a London bus – either a "hop on hop off" trip or a
    continuous journey.

4   Take our special shopping tour with lunch included in the
    price.

F R E E   D I S C O U N T   V O U C H E R S

Make the most of the sights of London with our book of free
discount vouchers to London's favourite places. At a much
reduced cost you can visit the London Zoo, the Planetarium and
Madame Tussaud's. If you want to tread on the hallowed turf of
Wembley now is your chance, and instead of being filled with
horror at the price, we can recommend the horrors of the Tower at our
expense.

If you wish to see a show or visit a nightspot, please note this
on your booking form.

At the end of a busy day you will want to come back to comfort and good

food. Praxi hotels offer comfortable rooms with tea/coffee making

facilities, television and private bathroom. Children under 14 receive

free accommodation if they share. Adult guests may dine in the superb

surroundings of our smart dining rooms and a full English breakfast is

included for the price paid.

Worked examples

PRAXITELES GROUP

A fictitious organisation for examination purposes only

PRAXITELES HOUSE · ADAM STREET · LONDON WC2N 6EZ
TELEPHONE 01 930 5115

Our ref   BF/md3

Your ref

(Date of typing)

The Manager
Betterprint Ltd
69 Blue Ford Lane
LONDON
SE21 5PP

Dear Sir

PRAXITELES HOUSE STATIONERY

I am pleased to acknowledge your recent letter.

It will without doubt be necessary for us to meet in order to discuss the
final look of our new logo. To this end I suggest Friday (Date appropriate
to date of typing) at 10 o'clock. If this is inconvenient please contact
Eileen Joyce, my assistant, who will arrange a further date and time.

We now have it in mind to bring the headed paper of all our other companies
into line with our own new stationery. However, we must ensure that people
do not get the various companies mixed up by having logos that are <u>too</u> alike.

It will be vital to ensure that they can be linked but not confused. I
suggest that we also discuss this point at our meeting. Perhaps you could
then get your artwork people to start as soon as possible on the new designs.

I must congratulate you and your staff on coming up with the goods so quickly.
I look forward to our meeting.

Yours faithfully
PRAXITELES HOUSE LTD

Bryan Ferrara
Marketing Manager

cc: Eileen Joyce

cc: Eileen Joyce ✔   (carbon copy)

cc: Eileen Joyce   (second carbon copy)

The Manager
Betterprint Ltd
69 Blue Ford Lane
LONDON
SE21 5PP

Ms E Joyce
Praxiteles House Ltd
Adam Street
London WC2N 6EZ

MEMORANDUM

From   Bryan Ferrara

To   Eileen Joyce

Ref   BF/md3

Date   (Date of typing)

<u>Urgent</u>

NEW LOGOS FOR HEADED PAPER

You will find enclosed a copy of a letter sent today to the Manager of Betterprint Ltd. Please note that I have asked him to contact you should the date I have suggested for the meeting not be convenient. Over the next 2 weeks, I am unavailable on 3 days. These are Tuesday of next week and Monday and Wednesday of the week after.

Can you please arrange an in-house meeting prior to the above meeting so that the opportunity is taken to get a full picture of any points that staff wish to raise. Would next Monday at either 10 am or 2 pm be possible?

I have received your report on the new advertising campaign. I agree that the new logo should be used and that the advertisement should go out at prime time if we are to get a good public response.

Can you please get to work on this as I believe that these slots are taken up very swiftly.

Enc

Task 2.3

MEMORANDUM

From David Hadfield, Sales Manager   *Ref* DH/A142

To   Ms Linda Wade   *Date* (DATE OF TYPING)
      Promotions Co-ordinator

SALES INFORMATION PACKAGE

At our recent departmental committee meeting it was resolved that
we should completely redesign our literature. Therefore a few
days ago I sent you a proposed price list. However, it was only
a draft copy and we now need to make some minor amendments.

Please notice that the charge for printing the same logo on both
front and back of a sweatshirt has had to be increased. An extra
£0.85 per garment will be added to the appropriate cost. Also
the price for each additional print colour will be £0.90.

Kindly emphasise that once we have received an order we can
guarantee delivery of clothing within four weeks.

In addition the children's range of sweatshirts will be extended.
Sizes CT1 (22" chest) and CT2 (24" chest) are available forthwith.

At the meeting the Managing Director suggested that we should
send clients small samples of material to demonstrate the superb
quality of our fabric. Another advantage is that each swatch
would show the range of colours we have available. This
certainly seems to be a good idea as customers are often confused
about the blue colours we offer. I therefore enclose an example
of the type of booklet we propose.

Please let me have an estimate of costs along with your views
about the feasibility of this plan. I must receive your opinions
immediately as prompt action needs taking.

Enc

Copy: Managing Director

Copy: Managing Director ✓   (CARBON COPY)

Copy: Managing Director   (SECOND CARBON COPY)

Ms Linda Wade
Promotions
Co-ordinator

PRAXITELES GROUP

A fictitious organisation for examination purposes only

PRAXITELES HOUSE · ADAM STREET · LONDON WC2N 6EZ
TELEPHONE 01 930 5115

Our ref   DH/Q963

Your ref   SM/ts

(DATE OF TYPING)

URGENT

Mrs S Moore
42 Anton Street
WIMBORNE
Dorset
BH21 7HL

Dear Mrs Moore

QUOTATION FOR SWEATSHIRTS

Thank you for your recent correspondence enquiring about the
cost of sweatshirts printed with your club's logo.

We confirm that for a minimum quantity of 50 shirts we would
charge £9.50 per garment. The enclosed catalogue has full
information about our pricing strategy. These charges are
inclusive of all artwork, stencil and set-up costs. Please
note that delivery will be within four weeks from receipt of
your order.

We are currently offering a 10% reduction on sweatshirts. To
qualify, your order should be received by us before (INSERT
DATE APPROPRIATE TO DATE OF TYPING).

We look forward to hearing from you.

Yours sincerely
PRAXIPRINT CLOTHING

David Hadfield
Sales Manager

Enc

URGENT

Mrs S Moore
42 Anton Street
WIMBORNE
Dorset
BH21 7HL

MEMORANDUM

From   Henry Kanta, Director   *Ref* HK/CCC

To   Sharon Sinclair, Accounts   *Date* (Date of typing)

<u>Priority</u>

CHILDLINE CHARITY CONCERT

The final arrangements are now in preparation for this concert to be held on Tuesday (Date appropriate to date of typing). Various members of the organising committee will be asking you to authorise payments over the next few days. If you have any queries about any of these please contact me immediately, as this must now be treated as urgent.

You may receive calls from the agents who represent the stars who are top of the bill. They are, of course, giving their services free. They will expect their expenses to be met. The 2 groups whose agents are likely to contact you are Bitter Harvest and Tricycle Clips. There may also be enquiries from the agents of these 3 artists about costs - Rory Galbraith, Bird Coltrane and Tanya Chitraj. If you need any more information concerning these, please contact me. Do not authorise any payments less than £50 or over £2000. I will leave it to your judgment as to whether the payment required seems fair. Consider the status of the artist or artists whose agent makes the claim.

I enclose a full list of artists giving their services for this event. If we have any cancellations, replacements or additional acts, I shall let you know at once.

Enc

cc: David Martin

cc: David Martin ✓   (carbon copy)

cc: David Martin   (second carbon copy)

PRAXITELES GROUP

A fictitious organisation for examination purposes only

PRAXITELES HOUSE · ADAM STREET · LONDON WC2N 6EZ

TELEPHONE 01 930 5115

Our ref   HK/AA/CCC

Your ref

(Date of typing)

Mr A Amir
Agency Manager
Acme Acts
North Hill
LONDON
NW57 7LH

Dear Mr Amir

TRICYCLE CLIPS - CHILDLINE CHARITY CONCERT

This is to confirm that all expenses will be paid for the group's
appearance at the Childline Benefit. Please pass on our deepest
thanks to them for offering their services free. I have no doubt
that they will be a very big draw, which will ensure as much
money as possible being raised for Childline.

Polygon Records hope to record the concert. They are prepared to
donate all profits. Please would you let me know if the group is
prepared to release any royalties from the record to Childline.
Will their current record company allow them temporary release
from contract for the recording to come out on the Hexagon
label?

Complimentary tickets for yourself and nine guests are enclosed.

Yours sincerely
PRAXITELES PROMOTIONS

Henry Kanta
Director

Encs

Mr A Amir
Agency Manager
Acme Acts
North Hill
LONDON
NW57 7LH

- -

Martin Black
Concert Organiser

Task 2.7

PRAXITELES GROUP

A fictitious organisation for examination purposes only

PRAXITELES HOUSE · ADAM STREET · LONDON WC2N 6EZ
TELEPHONE 01 930 5115

Our ref   PC/Store

Your ref

(DATE OF TYPING)

URGENT

Mr T R Harrison
Renting Manager
Prospect Commercial
14 Ramsey Road
READING   RG7 4AF

Dear Mr Harrison

STORAGE AT RACEDOWN FARM

Following our recent visit and telephone conversation with you, we are
now able to state our exact storage requirements. We should like to
rent the sheds for a period of four months starting on Friday
(INSERT DATE APPROPRIATE TO DATE OF TYPING). The farmer concerned has
very kindly agreed to unload and load the lorries so we will pay a £2
handling charge per pallet. These expenses will be payable to Mr Strong
upon receipt of his invoice. We shall try to give two days' notice of
any movement into or out of the building.

We are sending a copy of this letter to Mr M Strong at Racedown Farm,
Oakley, Basingstoke, RG23 7XT for information purposes.

The draft lease is enclosed. Please note that the only minor alteration
we require concerns the section about insurance. We trust that this
amendment will be in order.

Please can you send us the appropriate paperwork ready for signature so
that we can complete the necessary documentation. It is vital that this
is undertaken as soon as possible since we wish to deliver the first load
next week.

We look forward to hearing from you.

Yours sincerely
PRAXITELES GROUP

Peter Connolly
Warehouse Manager

Enc

cc Mr Strong

cc Mr Strong ✓   (CARBON COPY)

cc Mr Strong   (SECOND CARBON COPY)

Mr M Strong
Racedown Farm
Oakley
BASINGSTOKE
RG23 7XT

URGENT

Mr T R Harrison
Renting Manager
Prospect Commercial
14 Ramsey Road
READING   RG7 4AF

MEMORANDUM

From	Peter Connolly	*Ref*	PC/Store/RF
To	Trevor Benham	*Date*	(DATE OF TYPING)

RACEDOWN FARM NEAR BASINGSTOKE

You will be pleased to hear that I have arranged temporary storage facilities at the above address.

Mr Strong has agreed to handle the pallets which means we shall not need to take our forklift to the farm. As we shall be paying a £2 charge per pallet to the farmer, we must keep an accurate record of the actual number of items involved. Please ensure this is organised satisfactorily.

I confirm that one shed is 260 square metres while the other is slightly smaller at 163 square metres.

I hope we can start delivering to the site next week. However, we need to complete the business documentation before we begin using the two sheds.

I shall send you further data including the full address, telephone number etc, when appropriate.

Worked examples

PRAXITELES GROUP

A fictitious organisation for examination purposes only

PRAXITELES HOUSE · ADAM STREET · LONDON WC2N 6EZ
TELEPHONE 01 930 5115

Our ref   MF/IC34

Your ref

(Date of typing)

CONFIDENTIAL

Ms Diane Galsworthy
Larch Way
FERNDOWN
Dorset
BH44 6HY

Dear Ms Galsworthy

PRAXI SUPREMA ICE CREAM MAKER

Thank you for your letter with copy for the Praxi Suprema
Information Book. Your draft wording is just what we were
looking for. It is very clear and concise and should make the
working of our new machine simple for users. I would, however,
recommend that we make the following changes so that there is no
ambiguity.

In the section headed "Making ice cream" change the words
"must be well amalgamated" to "should be well mixed".

In the section headed "Cleaning" change "inner surface" to
"protective coating".

In the section headed "Safety in the home" change "on any hot
surface" to "on or near any source of heat".

I cannot see that any further changes will be necessary to your
copy. If you agree these, the booklet can go to print by (Monday
of the week after next).

Your original draft is enclosed for alteration. Please contact
my secretary, Elmer Dodd, if you have any queries.

Yours sincerely
PRAXI HOUSEWARES PLC

Marcus Finkelstein

Enc

CONFIDENTIAL

Ms Diane Galsworthy
Larch Way
FERNDOWN
Dorset
BH44 6HY

Mr Marcus Finkelstein
Praxi Housewares Plc
Praxiteles House
Adam Street
LONDON
WC2N 6EZ

MEMORANDUM

From Marcus Finkelstein   *Ref* MF/IC35

To   Mary Josephs   *Date* (Date of typing)

PRAXI SUPREMA ICE CREAM MAKER

I have today received copy for the instruction book for this new machine from Ms Diane Galsworthy. Apart from a few minor changes this seems just what we wanted. I shall ask her to agree to these changes, and we should then be ready to go to print.

Please can you confirm that copy for the Recipe Guide is also ready? The two can then go together and have the same cover illustration. I suggest that we ask the printers to go for a size of approximately 5 inches wide by 8 inches deep.

I must arrange to see you to check through all the other arrangements in connection with the launch. Will either next Wednesday at 10 am or 3 pm be a convenient appointment for you?

The actual launch date has not yet been made final. Would you let me know of any date during the next two months when you would be unable to attend? Many thanks for your help. We could not have managed to get these booklets ready without your hard work.

cc: Sales Promotions

cc: Sales Promotions ✓   (carbon copy)

cc: Sales Promotions   (second carbon copy)

PRAXITELES GROUP

A fictitious organisation for examination purposes only

PRAXITELES HOUSE · ADAM STREET · LONDON WC2N 6EZ
TELEPHONE 01 930 5115

Our ref CN/427C

Your ref

(Date of typing)

CONFIDENTIAL

Mr D Leslie
Abbass House
WESTCLIFF-ON-SEA
Essex
SSO 4AX

Dear Mr Leslie

Court Appearance for Speeding Offence

We have now had the opportunity to look through your statement in relation to
the charge of speeding on the Andover to Salisbury road. There is clear evidence
that you were travelling at 20 miles per hour above the relevant limit. It
would appear that you will have to plead guilty to the offence of exceeding
the speed limit.

We would like to receive details of the approximate mileage you travel
annually. Please also supply any other details which you believe may be
useful. For instance, you should say if you could lose your job if your
licence was taken away for any period of time.

Subject to any endorsements already on your licence, you may be given 3
penalty points and also be fined. However, if you have committed 2 or more
offences then you may lose your licence. We shall obviously need to have
full details of your motoring record.

The case will be heard in Andover Magistrates' Court. This is listed for
Wednesday (Date appropriate to date of typing) at 10 am. The above information
is therefore needed urgently and we enclose an addressed label for your reply.

Yours sincerely
PRAXITELES GROUP

Christopher Nix
Solicitor

Enc

cc: Ms Phillips

cc: Ms Phillips ✔   (Carbon copy)

cc: Ms Phillips   (Second Carbon copy)

Mr Christopher Nix
Solicitor
Praxiteles Group
Praxiteles House
Adam Street
LONDON WC2N 6EZ
- - - - - - - - - -
CONFIDENTIAL

Mr D Leslie
Abbass House
WESTCLIFF-ON-SEA
Essex
SSO 4AX

MEMORANDUM

From Christopher Nix   *Ref*   CN/427C

To Davina Phillips   *Date*   (Date of typing)

Please make an urgent diary note to attend the court hearing for Mr Leslie. I attach a copy of the letter which I have today sent to him so that you can extract details of place, time and date.

I appreciate that the case will be heard in Andover Magistrates' Court and this will mean you have to travel by train. However, the case is listed for 10 am. It may be possible for you to return to London by 2 pm to avoid the loss of the whole day's work. The firm will, of course, pay your expenses in full.

Once I have all the data I shall give you the file.

Mr Leslie will be pleading guilty to the charge but I still think we need to discuss the matter. Please contact my secretary to arrange a time for this.

Enc

Worked examples

MEMORANDUM

From   Elaine Griffiths   *Ref*   EG/CD7

To   Jason Markham   *Date*   (Date of typing)

CLASSICAL COMPACT DISC COMPETITION WINNERS

The results of the above competition have now been decided and are as follows.

The first prize of the complete set of Wagner's "Ring" cycle has been awarded to Malcolm Beardshaw.   The second prize of two Mozart operas goes to Jane Handley.   The third prize of the four Brahms symphonies goes to Mary Bradley.   You will find details of the winners' home addresses and telephone numbers on the attached copy letter sent to them today.   All prizes are from the Polygon catalogue of recordings.

Presentation of the prizes will be on Wednesday (Date appropriate to date of typing) at 10 am in the Romney committee room.   Please would you arrange for the usual refreshments - coffee, biscuits etc - to be laid on and served by 9.30 am.   Please also arrange for all staff who need to be present to be informed of the date, time and venue immediately.   I should contact them in person - there is no need to put it in writing.

A representative from Polygon Records will present the prizes and we also hope to have Sir James Priddy, the conductor, with us on the day.   As this has yet to be confirmed, make a provisional booking for him at the presentation.   As you know, each set of compact discs will be a signed edition.   Please check the signatures on each set before they are wrapped.

Enc

PRAXITELES GROUP

A fictitious organisation for examination purposes only

PRAXITELES HOUSE · ADAM STREET · LONDON WC2N 6EZ
TELEPHONE 01 930 5115

Our ref EG/CD4

Your ref PR63/SJP

PERSONAL

(Date of typing)

Mr Tom Perry
Classics Manager
Polygon Records
BIRMINGHAM
B97 4PQ

Dear Mr Perry

COMPACT DISC PRESENTATIONS

Details of the winners of the compact disc competition are on the
enclosed copy letter. The presentation is scheduled for 10 am
next Wednesday and will be in Praxiteles House in the Romney
committee room.

This letter is to confirm that we shall pay your expenses in full,
and also those for Sir James, if he is able to attend. Please
would you let me know by return if either of you will require
overnight accommodation on Tuesday night. I will then get my
secretary to make the necessary reservations.

I look forward to seeing you next week. Please let me know at
once if there is any further information you require.

Yours sincerely
PRAXITELES PROMOTIONS

Harriet Foot
Director

Enc

cc: Jason Markham

cc: Jason Markham ✓   (carbon copy)

cc: Jason Markham   (second carbon copy)

PERSONAL

Mr Tom Perry
Classics Manager
Polygon Records
BIRMINGHAM
B97 4PQ

- - - - - - - - - - - - - - - -

Cathy Hands
Publicity

Task 2.15

PRAXITELES GROUP

A fictitious organisation for examination purposes only

PRAXITELES HOUSE · ADAM STREET · LONDON WC2N 6EZ
TELEPHONE 01 930 5115

Our ref ST/LC/C48

Your ref

(Date of typing)

Mr P Brook
Personnel Manager
Astra Associates
110 Elm Street
BASINGSTOKE
RG23 9RW

Dear Mr Brook

FRENCH FOR BUSINESS AND PLEASURE

Thank you for your recent enquiry about our short courses.

We firmly believe that the language skills of the workforce in Britain may well be the decisive factor when competing in Europe. We are sure it will be necessary to be able to speak and understand at least one major foreign language.

In the introductory unit we spend most time on spoken communication. By the end of the course we expect students to be able to welcome and entertain foreign people. They should also be able to exchange simple information about themselves and their firm.

Miss Ryde, who is a language specialist, will contact your organisation to discuss the matter further. She will make an appointment with your Marketing Manager, Mr Dalton, within the next few days. In the meantime, we confirm that we could run a French course starting at 6.15 pm and finishing at 7.45 pm.

Please contact us again if you require any further details. At Praxiteles we aim to provide the very best language training.

Yours sincerely
PRAXITELES GROUP

(Mrs) Simone Thomas
EUROPEAN LANGUAGES SECTION

Copy to: Miss Ryde

Copy to: Miss Ryde   (Carbon copy)

Copy to: Miss Ryde   (Second carbon copy)

Task 2.16

MEMORANDUM

From S Thomas   *Ref* ST/C4

To Miss J Ryde   *Date* (Date of typing)

URGENT

Short Courses in French

I know you will be pleased to read the enclosed letter from one of our clients, Cox (UK) PLC of Woking. It is an excellent reference for the course. I like the Managing Director's comment that even he coped!

As you can see, they would now like us to timetable a second course on Mondays, starting on (Date appropriate to date of typing). You will note the class size will have to be increased from 12 full-time employees to 14. Please contact them as soon as possible to discuss the matter.

Please also contact Mr Dalton, who is the Marketing Manager of a firm called Astra Associates in Basingstoke. I enclose a copy of the letter I have written to them and shall be pleased if you will treat the matter as urgent. The number is Basingstoke 3878272.

You must be delighted with the way your department is developing. The monthly reports are very encouraging.

Encs

Mr P Brook
Personnel Manager
Astra Associates
110 Elm Street
BASINGSTOKE
RG23 9RW

URGENT

Miss J Ryde
Court House

44

THE ROYAL SOCIETY OF ARTS
EXAMINATIONS BOARD
SINGLE-SUBJECT EXAMINATIONS

W287
TYPEWRITING SKILLS
STAGE II (INTERMEDIATE)
THURSDAY 19 MAY 1988

PART 1 (TIME ALLOWED - ONE AND A QUARTER HOURS)

Notes for candidates

1   Please write or type your name and centre number on each piece of your work.

2   Please assemble your completed work in the order in which it is presented in this paper and cross through any work which you do not wish to be marked.

3   Calculators, English Dictionaries and manufacturers' machine manuals may be used in the examinations.

4   This paper includes Tasks 1 and 2; Task 3 will be handed to you during the course of the examination.

You must:

1   Complete all three tasks.

2   Use only the stationery provided in your answer book.

3   Insert today's date on letters and memos, unless otherwise instructed.

(Penalties will be incurred if these instructions are not followed)

TSII-1(Whitsun 1988)

Part 1 Exam

TASK 1

Praxi Race Club — *Use Spaced Caps — do not underline*

News Bulletin — *Use Closed Caps — please underline*

At the recent Annual General Meeting we were pleased by the election of Mrs Amy Smythe-Carruthers to the Committee. She is renowned for her work for/and sponsorship/ *charity* *and will be an able new member.*

It is possible that a notable Member of Parliament could have a mount in the Amateur Riders' Race the "OXO" on Saturday 22 October 1988. || The visit arranged to Malton Stables in November should be ~~interesting.~~ *of great interest.* First-time-out winners continue to be a feature of the stable and there were 7 such successes last season and only 3 of the 26 individual winning horses failed to oblige within their/three *first* races. The horses are almost always fit when setting foot on the race course and this applies particularly to the early two-year olds who win first or second time out if they have any ability.

well-known peer
A ~~notable personality~~ will present the Praxi Gold Cup at the March Meeting next year.

Some miniature replicas in bronze of the famous Red Rum may be made available to the Club in the near future. Possible cost £120 each. (Actual size 11½" x 6" x 3½ in overall.)

Due to the success of the last Xmas Dinner Dance the Committee has decided to use the same venue together with a similar programme. We are hoping that the MENZ Trio and the local brass band will entertain us once more. Further details will be (be) circulated to *all current* members in the ~~near future.~~ *due course.*

The Club is very excited at its proposed new venture, the syndication of a thoroughbred yearling "MERRY QUIP". See separate leaflet /for *more details. soon*

May I take this opportunity to wish you a successful season's punting.

J A Taylor
Race Club Secretary

May 1988

leave 3 clear line spaces above & below this para

TASK 2

Our ref JAT/412

Mr M Parkhurst JP
19 Old Coach Road
MARKET RASEN
Lincolnshire
LN1 4BU

Typist - label to Mr P - mark Personal

Dr Mr Parkhurst
Praxi Race Club Membership 1988-89

Use Closed Caps - do not underline

The (annual) subscription is now ~~almost~~ due for 1988/89 starting from 1 August 1988. The fees have increased ✓ slightly ~~moderately~~ on last year and are:

	£
Single	140
Man and wife	200
Junior (under 18)	80

Type in double line spacing please

For yr info I enclose details of fixed meetings and some proposed trips for the coming season. A sep form is enclosed for you to complete if you wish to attend any of the extra visits.

The News Bulletin is enclosed and details of a new venture - the syndication of a thoroughbred yearling.

On (receit) of your cheque your badge(s) etc will be sent to you forthwith. Please return within two weeks of the date of this letter ie (Typist - please insert date for Friday of next week). // I wish all you a (sucessful) new season.

Yrs sincerely

J A Taylor
Club Sec

THE ROYAL SOCIETY OF ARTS
EXAMINATIONS BOARD
SINGLE-SUBJECT EXAMINATIONS

W287

TYPEWRITING SKILLS

STAGE II (INTERMEDIATE)

THURSDAY 19 MAY 1988

<u>INSTRUCTIONS TO INVIGILATOR</u>

<u>PART 1</u>

(a) Read to the candidates the Instructions.

(b) Hand to each candidate a copy of the <u>White</u> Part 1 Examination
Paper and an answer book (Code U).

(c) When the candidates are ready, start the examination.

(d) After about 15-30 minutes, if possible when most candidates have
work in their machines, place on each candidate's desk a copy of
Task 3, the <u>Green</u> paper.

THE ROYAL SOCIETY OF ARTS
EXAMINATIONS BOARD
SINGLE-SUBJECT EXAMINATIONS

W287 TYPEWRITING SKILLS
STAGE II (INTERMEDIATE)
THURSDAY 19 MAY 1988

PART 1 - TASK 3

TSII - 1 (Whitsun 1988)

(Memo)

To   C R Broadhurst   Race Course Manager
From   J A Taylor   Club Secretary
Ref   JAT/mm

(Typist – copies
Treasurer + file
– indicate routing)

I have written to all ~~our~~ current members
and enclose / copies for your information:

A   Letter, forthcoming race dates,
     (details also) of the new
     venture in the syndication of
     the yearling and the News ~~Bulletin~~ Article.

✓

B   Details of monies raised for Charities
     1986/87.

C   (Aplication) form for the extra visits
     and for shares in the yearling
     " ___ ___ " . (Typist insert name of
yearling)

I sh let you know as soon as all the replies
are returned . // At our last Cttee meeting we
spoke of a private bar being made available
for members of the Club. Has there been any ~~progress~~ more information
on this yet? Wd it be poss for us to meet
before the next Committee meeting scheduled for
Aug so that we can (discus) this point, along
with some others I have in mind?

Encs

(Typist –
label to
Mr Broadhurst
Grandstand office
Praxi Race Club)

52

PRACTICE FOR PART 2 EXAMS

Notes to candidates

Draft notices for display

In this type of task you will be required to use different styles of capitals, to leave some space clear, and to change the layout of the material, eg to move a block of wording to another position round the space to be left for an illustration.

You will also be asked to emphasise certain words, eg 'Give prominence to the last line'. For this purpose you may use capitals, underlining or any other feature available on the typewriter you are using, eg reverse image or emboldening.

One word which occurs more than once throughout the draft will have to be changed by you to a different word given in the instructions.

Aim to type, check and correct this type of task within 25 minutes   `25.00`

Ruled tables

This type of task tests your ability to present material in columns as well as continuous text.

You will also need to be careful how you allocate space around the columns and other wording in order to give yourself room to rule as shown in the draft.

Aim to type, check and correct this type of task within 30 minutes   `30.00`

Forms for completion

In the Stage II exams, as in this book, details may not be given in the same order as the headings in the pre-printed form.

Do not forget to make any deletions clearly. Do not sign the forms you type.

RSA forms for typing the tasks in this book are available from bookshops in the Stationery Pad Book Two. In the exam, you will be provided with two copies of the form, in case you spoil your first attempt.

Aim to type, check and correct this type of task within 10 minutes   `10.00`

3 Draft notices for display

Task 3.1

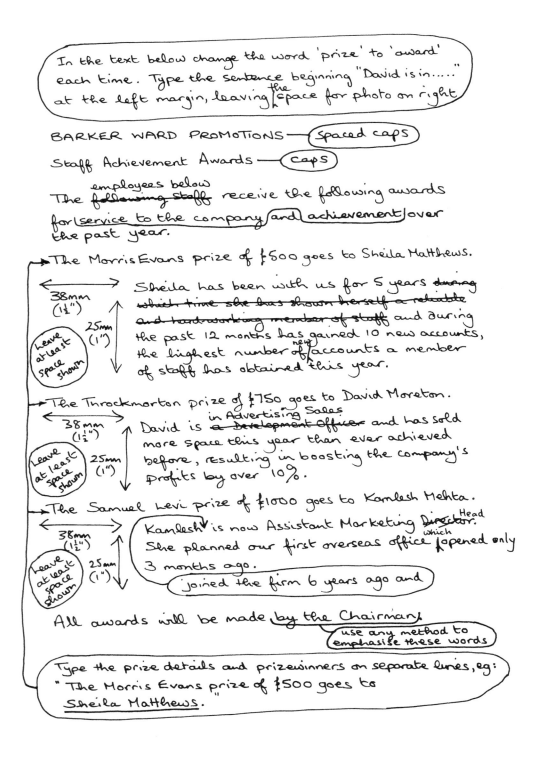

In the text below change the word 'prize' to 'award' each time. Type the sentence beginning "David is in....." at the left margin, leaving the space for photo on right

BARKER WARD PROMOTIONS — spaced caps

Staff Achievement Awards — caps

The ~~following staff~~ employees below receive the following awards for service to the company and achievement over the past year.

The Morris Evans prize of £500 goes to Sheila Matthews.

38mm (1½")   25mm (1")   Leave at least space shown

Sheila has been with us for 5 years ~~during which time she has shown herself a reliable and hardworking member of staff~~ and during the past 12 months has gained 10 new accounts, the highest number of new accounts a member of staff has obtained this year.

The Throckmorton prize of £750 goes to David Moreton.

38mm (1½")   25mm (1")   Leave at least space shown

David is ~~a Development Officer~~ in Advertising Sales and has sold more space this year than ever achieved before, resulting in boosting the company's profits by over 10%.

The Samuel Levi prize of £1000 goes to Kamlesh Mehta.

38mm (1½")   25mm (1")   Leave at least space shown

Kamlesh is now Assistant Marketing ~~Director~~ Head. She joined the firm 6 years ago and planned our first overseas office which opened only 3 months ago.

All awards will be made by the Chairman   use any method to emphasise these words

Type the prize details and prizewinners on separate lines, eg: " The Morris Evans prize of £500 goes to Sheila Matthews."

54

At the points marked ⬍ leave a space at least 50mm (2") wide by 63 mm (2½") high for a photograph. Change the word 'book' to 'novel' each time it occurs.

NEW PUBLICATIONS FOR THE NEW YEAR — spaced caps

Three New Novels To Be Published Early Next Year

Henry and Antonia by Garton Moore ◄

A contemporary love story spanning the years 1948-1988, the theme of the book ~~which tells of the deep and lasting relationship between a pair who have grown up together~~ is the (comforts) and the (stresses) caused by the ~~courtship and~~ pairing of two kindred spirits.

emotional and physical

Published by Praxiteles & Praxiteles at £10.95 ◄

The Dawn by Ellison Petersen ◄

A tale of horror in contemporary Britain, the book presents a vision of the country gripped by madness at dawn.

which is at its most terrifying

Published by Hardwick Hennessy at £7.95 ◄

Mary Dunnock's Pig by Charles Montgomery ◄

An absolutely ~~riotous~~ hilarious comedy set during the war, this book relates the efforts of a town's most respected citizen to conceal an "illegal" pig.

Published by Edwards & Mason at £9.95 ◄

All three novels are published on 31 January — this line in caps

Leave no space here

Order your copy now! — use any method to give prominence to this line

Change layout so that book, author and publication details appear _above_ the description, in the following form:

Garton Moore : "Henry and Antonia"
Published by Praxiteles & Praxiteles at £10.95

A contemporary....... "

Change the layout of the table to
show 'Catalogue Number' as the 1st column,
and column headings in capitals, as in the
following example:

CATALOGUE NUMBER   ITEM   PRICE

PNWFP35   Winter flowering pansy   £1.90 per tray

. . . .

Change the words "flowers" } to { "plants" each time.
             "flower" }   { "plant"

Gardener's World ——— (spaced caps)

Some Ideas For Winter Hanging Baskets

Most people ~~have the idea~~ *seem to think* that hanging baskets can only be put up in the summer. However, there are now a considerable number of hardy and evergreen flowers [that can be put in baskets] for outside display and which ~~survive and will bloom~~ throughout the seasons.

Here are some ideas ~~that may inspire you if you want winter for baskets which will fit your gas terra it all of~~ the sorts of flowers you can use together with ~~their Nursery references~~ and prices. The 2 most popular are [their catalogue numbers] illustrated below.

Item	Catalogue number and price	
Winter flowering pansy	PNWFP35	£1.90 per tray
Miniature hebe	PNHEB45	£1.20 each
Purple heather	PNHEA55	£1.95 each
Trailing ivy	PNTRI65	£1.25 per pot
Mixed polyanthus	PNPOL75	£1.95 per tray
Periwinkle	PNPER85	£2.50 each

(Leave at least 13 mm (½"))

Winter flowering pansy ←——→ Miniature hebe
(Leave at least 38 mm (1½"))   (Leave at least 13 mm (½"))

To purchase any flower mentioned above, call in at our premises or fill in an order form and return it without delay.

(give prominence to these words)

Put prize headings on one line with initial capitals and underscore as in this example:

Suprema Ice Cream Maker

Leave a space at least 50 mm (2") wide by 50 mm (2") deep for a photograph at each point marked *

Commencing next Friday — *this line in caps*

GARRETTS SPRING EVENT

Spaced caps

Change the word 'sale' to 'event' each time it occurs

Our annual spring sale commences next week and as a valued account holder, you are invited to attend the special preview evening. Please bring your invitation with you to the preview night, as it will be entered in our sale draw — you could be the lucky winner of one of the following magnificent prizes!

and hand it in at the door

Suprema
ice cream maker

Will make up to one litre of ice cream in less than 30 minutes; full recipes, will of course be found in packaging. *are included*   *

Magichef
food processor

*   Comes complete with attachments for vegetable slicing and grating and has a capacity of 2 litres.

Percofilta
coffee maker

Makes perfect filter coffee in 3 minutes and keeps it piping hot *as long as you want* for an indefinite period — comes with a permanent filter cone so there is no need to keep buying papers filters.   *

use any method to highlight these words

All sale goods are genuinely discounted and first quality unless otherwise marked.

4 Ruled tables

Task 4.1

WAYFARER WALKING WEEKENDS

Why not take a break with an excellent value
Wayfarer Walking Weekend?

rule as shown

Approximate Distance Covered	Degree of Difficulty	Accommodation	
		Hotel	Cost
Cotswolds			
16 miles - - - - - - -	Easy	Beacon	£50
30 miles - - - - -	Demanding	Cleeve	£40
25 miles - - - -	Moderate	Malvern	£38
18 miles - - -	Easy	Dixton	£35
Fenlands		own arrangements to be made by walkers** *	
18 miles - - -	Easy		
10 miles - - --	Easy *		
Yorkshire Dales			
28 miles -	Demanding	Austwick	£38
22 miles	Moderate	Beck	£32
20 miles	Moderate	Moat	£40
21 miles	Demanding	Hilltop	£41

within each section re-arrange distance of walks into ascending order. Leave the 3 sections in alphabetical order as shown

** No formal arrangement yet negotiated
* Suitable for the disabled

Begin your break on Friday evening ~~with a welcome drink~~.
The cost includes 3-course dinner, bed and breakfast for 2
nights (double room with shower). ~~Your hotel has agreed~~ packed lunches are provided
~~to provide packed lunches~~ on Saturday and Sunday. An experienced guide walks
with your group ~~(usually about 10 people)~~ so you can forget
about map reading, enjoy the scenery and relax.

and tea is served early Sunday evening, before you leave

58

PRAXITELES CLOTHING STORE - Telephone 792167

SCHOOL OUTFITTERS DEPARTMENT - Extension 268

We are your local approved school uniform suppliers - use us!
~~Our supplies are just what you require soon~~
We hope the following will give you some idea of our prices of
uniform for the forthcoming year. To be assured of all your
requirements, remember to shop early. We also have ~~good ranges~~
sports equipment and Scout & Guide uniforms.

Please re-arrange the order of the 'Boys' and 'Girls' columns
so that 'Girls' is the 2nd column and 'Boys' is the 3rd column

Uniform for I - V Years only	Prices *		Colour Combinations
	Boys	Girls	
Outdoor			
Blazer - - - - -	£75.39 £73.68	£77.50 £75.50	Maroon Black
Raincoat - - - -	£37.95 £36.85	£39.55 £38.45	Maroon Black
Indoor			
Skirt - - - -	—	£17.60	
Trousers - - - - -	£18.35	£16.10	Charcoal grey
Cardigan	£17.50	£18.60	
Pullover - - - - -	£15.35	£16.30	Grey
Blouse - - -	—	£15.40	Pink + white check (Girls)
Shirt - - -	£14.30	—	White or grey (Boys)
~~Sports~~ ~~Football strip, blouses vests, shorts, socks & and boots - price range boots will be given on request~~	Prices for football shirt,		Maroon/white
Accessories School badges, ties and belt purses are readily available, prices from - - -	£5.~~28~~ 67	£5.~~67~~ 75	Maroon/black/gold

* Prices vary according to size   Rule as shown

Ruled tables

JETCRAFT
PARTY PLAN JEWELLERY

This high quality range is (fashionable yet elegant).
Jetcraft Jewellery ~~proudly~~ presents the 'Gladstone' range.
Your customers will appreciate the excellent value
our goods represents. We can offer such good
value by selling direct to you. You in turn can
offer tremendous value by selling direct to
customers in their own homes. ~~The discount~~ See table
~~for the~~ attractive discount you will receive
~~we give to you is shown below~~. In addition
prizes are awarded each quarter for the highest
sales figures. , both for themselves and as gifts for others

A presentation pack for use at your Jetcraft parties
is being despatched under separate cover ~~and should~~
~~arrive within 5 days~~ by registered post.

Wishing you every success

rule as shown

Re-arrange each set of 'names' of jewellery in alphabetical order

| 'Gladstone' Range | Available in | | Discount Percentage Given |
	Gold*	Silver	
Brooches			
Alison	gold	--	30%
Daphne	gold	silver	30%
Eve	--	silver	25%
Catherine	gold	silver	30%
Necklaces			
Jessica	gold plated only		25%
Jasmin	silver plated only		25%
Rings			
Julia	gold	silver	30%
Rose	gold	silver	30%
Louisa	--	silver	20%
Stephanie	--	silver	20%

*9 carat

PRAXITELES PUBLIC LIMITED COMPANY (Rule as shown)

Subsidiary Companies[1]	Operations and Involvement		Country of Registration
	Activity	Allotted Share Capital	
Primary			
Praxiteles (South) Limited	Specialised equipment provider	100% Ordinary	England
Manx (Plastics) Limited . . .	Plastic mouldings	51% Common	Isle of Man
PXT (International) Limited	Cellular telephones	70% Common	Canada
Related			
PXT (Edinburgh) Limited . .	Plastic stopper caps	30% Ordinary	Scotland
Praxiteles Incorporated [2] . .	Plastic mouldings	100% Common	United States of America
~~Staff superannuation scheme~~	~~Pension benefits~~ now closed to ~~new entrants~~		
Plastics (PXT) Limited . . .	Plastic coatings	100% Ordinary	England
Staff			
Employees' shares (, and two share option schemes for ~~its~~ their employees)	All Praxiteles Companies have established one share ownership scheme. The option schemes are savings related exercisable between 2 and 5 years from grant.		These schemes are basically European. The Americas have separate arrangements.

A wholly-owned subsidiary.

2 ~~With shares divided on a 30% Equity basis~~

[1] Brief details of principal subsidiaries and related companies with confirmation of group arrangements for employees, including those who worked (mainly or wholly) outside the United Kingdom and whose remuneration was in excess of £30,000.

(Re-arrange the categories so that Primary is first, Staff second + Related is third AND re-arrange the items within each category alphabetically.)

PRAXIHOUSES

STYLISH NEW HOMES AT BRAMPTON PARK

Style	Colour Scheme*		Number Available
	Ground Floor	First Floor	
Detached House			
Stratford	Mint	Beige	18
Gloucester	Beige	White	15
Kendal	Almond	Lilac	20
Lincoln	White	Lilac	16
Bungalow			
Canterbury . . .	Mint throughout		10
Winchester . . .	Beige throughout		14
Carlisle . . .	Grey throughout		12
Semi-detached House			
Telford . .	Grey	Lilac	8
Gainsborough	White	White	2
Chester	Mint	Almond	5

rule as shown

within each category, re-arrange in descending order of number available

*Unless otherwise arranged

Full details are available in the showhouse ~~reception area~~.

The emphasis is on detached houses for young families. Notable features include ~~lots of storage space~~ and ~~ample power points~~.

The semi-detached houses are less numerous and built with young couples in mind. ~~Again they are built to~~ These are also spacious and have sensible storage as a standard provision ~~a very practical specification.~~ an attractive, easily maintained garden, generous room sizes,

Bungalows also feature strongly and are tastefully designed for those wishing to live on one level. ~~They are particularly suitable for the~~

Brampton Park is the latest Praxihouses development.

PREMIER CLASS HOLIDAYS   (Please rule as shown)

Departure Airport *	Lakes and Mountains of Italy		Month and Duration
	Hotels	Excursions	
Celebration Bonus			
Gatwick	Anniversary and Honeymoon Special saving per person on 14 night holidays (and extra grand mystery tour full of romance!		16 July – 26 August 14 nights (7 nights also available)
Manchester			25 April – 6 July 14 nights
Heathrow	(in selected hotels with special arrangements at hotel,		1 March – 24 April 14 nights
Highly Recommended			
→Luton	Excelsior	Wednesdays	1 – 26 October 10 nights
Special			
Heathrow	Rosemarie	To be announced twice weekly	7 nights or 14 nights 20 May – 10 June
→Manchester	Palace	Mondays	(26) September – (22) October 7 nights
Gatwick	Grand (~~also at The Suzanne~~)	Tuesdays and Thursdays – Various	19 May – 22 June 14 nights only (~~10 nights at The Suzanne~~)

* A reduction will be made for certain journeys if taken by train. ~~This reduction~~ Therefore, there will be two nights less at the hotel, one each end of the holiday. ~~will not be available during the peak months~~

(Re-arrange the 3 categories so that 'Special' is first, 'Celebration Bonus' is second and 'Highly Recommended' is third, AND re-arrange alphabetically the items within each category)

HOLDERS HOLIDAYS
TOURING CARAVAN SPECIALISTS

Why queue at the airport this year? Bring your caravan to one of our ~~very~~ clean, spacious sites and enjoy superb facilities. Our supermarkets offer a wide range of goods. *(including newspapers, freshly baked bread and fresh meat)* A ~~takeaway food service and snack bar~~ are available 7 days a week. Sports facilities include swimming, badminton and tennis. ~~Crazy golf is available at most sites.~~ The ~~small friendly~~ licensed clubs will happily cater for children. ~~Our small friendly clubs can quench your thirst.~~ A laundrette is open 24 hours a day.

rule as shown

Touring Caravan Site	Minimum Stay (Nights)	Available From	To
Lake District			
Appleby	2	April	September
Ambleside	3	May	September
Kendal	4	April	October
Cockermouth	3	June	August
West Country			
Perranporth	6	Open all year *	
Dawlish	4	Closed only at Christmas	
East Anglia			
Newmarket	1	March	November
Sheringham	3	April	November
Saffron Walden	2	April	October
Aldeburgh	2	March	October

within each section, re-arrange place names in alphabetical order.

* Special Christmas breaks a feature

Caravans are available for hire at very reasonable rates. Please telephone for further details.

PRAXITELES FARM

Re-arrange order of Cows alphabetically by names in first column, and re-arrange Pigs numerically, starting with the lowest number in there first column.

INTERIM SERVICING AND NUMBERS REPORT

Code (Name or Number)	Served by		Number Born and Codes Allocated
	1st Service	2nd Service	
Sheep * Thirty blue raddle marked carrying singles Twenty green raddle marked carrying multiples Twenty red raddle marked carrying twins	Three rams served each group.		Thirty singles, Pen 6B Seven sets of triplets, Pen 4G Twenty sets of twins, nine sets of quads, four sets of quins, Pen 5R
Pigs O801 - - - - - O147 - - - - - OO73 - - - - - 0905 - - - - 0318 - - - - -	Harold George Henry Richard Ronald	Richard Jack Ronald George Henry	Twelve, BB801 Fifteen, XX147 Twelve, WW905 Fourteen, NN073 Eight, RR318
~~N538~~ ~~M694~~			~~Ten, NN538~~ ~~Nine, MM694~~
Cows Buttercup Daisy Clover Dandelion Poppy	All served by Bull BB9 (hired from Roundlewhyke Farm)		One, Bp3751 One, Dy3752 One, Cr3753 One, Dn3754 One, Py3755

* The main flock had been split into three groups, each served by three different rams. ~~Any ewes not served in group 1 were put into~~ ~~Ewes that had not taken the ram were moved on~~ group 2, and so on for group 3.

Rule as shown

5 Forms for completion

Complete a Remittance Advice form. You may type all entries in capitals if you wish.

To Jackson, Carlton + Co, 104 Old Square, PULBOROUGH, West Sussex RH10 6EK

with a ~~bank credit~~ ~~cheque enclosed~~ for the following: ✓

Invoice No	dated	for	
34856	19.11.19—	for	£345.00
27345	1.10.19—	"	£17.25
27543	6.10.19—	"	£11.75
35100	1.12.19—	"	£115.00
35269	10.12.19—	"	£57.50
35312	12.12.19—	"	£23.00
			£569.50

Task 5.2

Complete an Order form. You may type all entries in capitals if you wish.

Ms P Foley at the Praxiteles Group, Branch Office, in London Road, CHICHESTER, West Sussex PO19 2FY requires the following items:

   6 reference DG506, card index files
   3 reference FL207, magazine files
   4 reference DG508, filing cabinets (~~3 drawers~~) ✓
   1 reference HP405, stand

Order the items from Regis Supplies Ltd, Terminus Industrial Estate, ALDINGBOURNE, West Sussex PO23 9PG.

The Order Number will be 28821. Ask them to deliver direct to the Branch Office.

The order will be signed in the Personnel Department

Please complete the order form and number it NG163.

The Sales Department would like the following items ordered from Williams Commercial Stationers, 3 Connaught Square, LONDON WC2 4EJ

(✓) 10 boxes of printed ~~memorandum~~ ~~memo forms~~ on continuous listing paper

1,000 printed business cards

50 reams A4 paper 75g weight

10 reams A4 paper 100g weight

2 doz loose leaf files

They can be delivered to the above address and are needed by end of the month.

You may type all entries in capitals if you wish

Complete an Enquiry form. You may type all entries in capitals if you wish.

To Office Furniture (Leasing) Ltd, 17 The Forum,
FISHBOURNE, West Sussex PO18 5JE

Our ref C34/89   Their ref AJ.hf
The reply is to be returned to Mr ~~R Harris~~ ~~A Jones~~ in the Contracts ✓
Department.

Details

Supply of 2 executive desks in sapele, vinyl or leather bound, leased over a 3 year term

Supply of 2 secretarial corner units in teak, leased over the same period

Complete the Enquiry Form with the following:

Send to G Henthorn & Co, 3 The Causeway, SIDCUP, Kent DA4 3BJ from the Purchasing Department (replies for the attention of Mr G Grimes)

The details are 4 executive office desks in oak ~~in teak~~.

Bookshelf attachments for above

4 leather swivel chairs with high backs

4 cream filing cabinets

2 plan filing cabinets in cream

2 wood and vinyl chairs

All entries may be typed in capitals if you wish

Task 5.6

Complete a Quotation form. You may type all entries in capitals if you wish.

Send the Quotation No 7005 to The Headmaster, Compton Community College, North Avenue East, BOGNOR REGIS, West Sussex PO23 8BC, his reference BT/SH, in reply to his enquiry dated 1 February 19—.

Quote the following:

SPORTSWEAR
1 Maroon and white football shirt   £15.50
1 pair white football shorts   £6.95
              £22.45

Prices include postage + packing.

Add a note to say that there is a further 5% discount on orders over £300.

Discount ~~£2.45~~ ✓
~~£2.25~~

£20.00

Complete the Action List for
the Fitted Kitchens Sector

from May to June for the
Staff

Contract EJ451 Grey

① with ~~dark oak facing~~ ~~mahogany~~ trims - J Brown

Contract EM 53$\overset{2}{\cancel{8}}$ All wood
~~farmhouse~~ kitchen - B Roscoe

Contract JY232 Swedish design
- units and sink only - G Baker

Contract JY234 Full Swedish
design ~~kitchen~~ (replace all
appliances) - K Crompton

Supplies to be drawn from
stores on Monday mornings ~~only~~.

Type in space
at foot of form

You may type all entries in
capitals if you wish

Forms for completion

Forms for completion

Complete the Job List sheet 2 of 2
for the week ending Friday last.

Printing Division need

✓ 1   3 ~~security locks~~ *yale keys* to be fitted
to stationery cupboards for
end of this week

4   Routine inspection to be
carried out of all electrical wiring
(as soon as possible)

3   Carpet tile to be replaced
immediately in reception

2   Window pane to be fitted in
reception immediately

you may type everything
in caps if you wish

Worked examples

3 Draft notices for display

```
B A R K E R   W A R D   P R O M O T I O N S

STAFF ACHIEVEMENT AWARDS

The employees below receive the following awards for achievement
and service to the company over the past year.

The Morris Evans award of £500 goes to
Sheila Matthews.

                Sheila has been with us for 5 years and during
                the past 12 months has gained 10 new accounts,
                the highest number of new accounts a member of
                staff has obtained this year.


The Throckmorton award of £750 goes to
David Moreton.

David is in Advertising Sales and has sold more
space this year than ever achieved before,
resulting in boosting the company's profits by
over 10%.


The Samuel Levi award of £1000 goes to
Kamlesh Mehta.

                Kamlesh joined the firm 6 years ago and is now
                Assistant Marketing Head.  She planned our
                first overseas office which opened only 3
                months ago.


All awards will be made by the Chairman.
```

```
N E W   P U B L I C A T I O N S   F O R   T H E   N E W   Y E A R
Three New Novels To Be Published Early Next Year

                Garton Moore: "Henry and Antonia"
                Published by Praxiteles & Praxiteles at
                £10.95

                A contemporary love story spanning the years
                1948-1988, the theme of the novel is the
                stresses and the comforts caused by the
                emotional and physical pairing of two kindred
                spirits.



Ellison Petersen: "The Dawn"
Published by Hardwick Hennessy at £7.95

A tale of horror in contemporary Britain,
the novel presents a vision of the country
gripped by madness which is at its most
terrifying at dawn.




                Charles Montgomery: "Mary Dunnock's Pig"
                Published by Edwards & Mason at £9.95

                An absolutely hilarious comedy set during the
                war, this novel relates the efforts of a
                town's most respected citizen to conceal an
                "illegal" pig.




ALL THREE NOVELS ARE PUBLISHED ON 31 JANUARY
Order your copy now!
```

Task 3.3

G A R D E N E R ' S   W O R L D

Some Ideas For Winter Hanging Baskets

Most people seem to think that hanging baskets can only be put up
in the summer. However, there are now a considerable number of
hardy and evergreen plants that can be put in baskets for outside
display and which will bloom and survive throughout the seasons.

Here are some ideas for the sorts of plants you can use together
with their catalogue numbers and prices. The 2 most popular are
illustrated below.

CATALOGUE NUMBER	ITEM	PRICE
PNWFP35	Winter flowering pansy	£1.90 per tray
PNHEB45	Miniature hebe	£1.20 each
PNHEA55	Purple heather	£1.95 each
PNTRI65	Trailing ivy	£1.25 per pot
PNPOL75	Mixed polyanthus	£1.95 per tray
PNPER85	Periwinkle	£2.50 each

Winter flowering
pansy

Miniature
hebe

To purchase any plant mentioned above, call in at our premises or
fill in an order form and **return it without delay.**

Task 3.4

COMMENCING NEXT FRIDAY

G A R R E T T S   S P R I N G   E V E N T

Our annual spring event commences next week. Please bring your
invitation with you to the preview night and hand it in at the
door as it will be entered in our event draw - you could be the
lucky winner of one of the following magnificent prizes!

Suprema Ice Cream Maker

Will make up to one litre of ice cream in
less than 30 minutes; full recipes are
included in packaging.

Magichef Food Processor

Comes complete with attachments for grating
and vegetable slicing and has a capacity of 2
litres.

Percofilta Coffee Maker

Makes perfect filter coffee in 3 minutes and
keeps it piping hot as long as you want -
comes with a permanent filter cone so there
is no need to keep buying filter papers.

All event goods **are genuinely discounted** and first quality unless
otherwise marked.

4 Ruled tables

Task 4.1

WAYFARER WALKING WEEKENDS

Why not take a break with an excellent value Wayfarer Walking Weekend?

Approximate Distance Covered	Degree of Difficulty	Accommodation	
		Hotel	Cost
Cotswolds			
16 miles	Easy	Beacon	£40
18 miles	Easy	Dixton	£35
25 miles	Moderate	Malvern	£38
30 miles	Demanding	Cleeve	£50
Fenlands			
10 miles	Easy*	Own arrangements to be made by walkers**	
18 miles	Easy		
Yorkshire Dales			
20 miles	Moderate	Moat	£40
21 miles	Demanding	Hilltop	£41
22 miles	Moderate	Beck	£32
28 miles	Demanding	Austwick	£38

*   Suitable for the disabled
** No formal arrangement yet negotiated

Begin your break on Friday evening. The cost includes 3-course dinner, bed and breakfast for 2 nights (double room with shower). Packed lunches are provided on Saturday and Sunday and tea is served early Sunday evening, before you leave. An experienced guide walks with your group so you can forget about map reading, relax and enjoy the scenery.

Task 4.2

PRAXITELES CLOTHING STORE - Telephone 792167

SCHOOL OUTFITTERS DEPARTMENT - Extension 268

We are your local approved school uniform suppliers - use us! We hope the following will give you some idea of our prices of uniform for the forthcoming year. To be assured of all your requirements, remember to shop early. We also have Scout and Guide uniforms and sports equipment.

Uniform for I - V Years only	Prices*		Colour Combinations
	Girls	Boys	
Outdoor			
Blazer	£39.55 £38.45	£37.95 £36.85	Maroon Black
Raincoat	£77.50 £75.50	£75.39 £73.68	Maroon Black
Indoor			
Cardigan	£18.60 £16.30	£17.50 £15.35	Grey
Pullover			
Skirt	£17.60 £16.10	- £18.35	Charcoal grey
Trousers			
Blouse	£15.40	- £14.30	Pink and white check (Girls) White or grey (Boys)
Shirt	-		
	Prices for football shirt, vests, shorts, socks and boots will be given on request		Maroon/white
Accessories			
School badges, ties and belt purses are readily available, prices from	£5.75	£5.67	Maroon/black/gold

* Prices vary according to size

Task 4.3

JETCRAFT

PARTY PLAN JEWELLERY

Jetcraft Jewellery presents the 'Gladstone' range. This high quality range is elegant yet fashionable. Your customers will appreciate the excellent value our goods represent, both for themselves and as gifts for others. We can offer such good value by selling direct to you. You in turn can offer tremendous value by selling direct to customers in their own homes. See table for the attractive discount you will receive. In addition prizes are awarded each quarter for the highest sales figures.

A presentation pack for use at your Jetcraft parties is being despatched under separate cover.

Wishing you every success

'Gladstone' Range	Available in		Percentage Discount Given
	Gold*	Silver	
Brooches		---	30%
Alison	gold	silver	30%
Catherine	gold	silver	30%
Daphne	gold	silver	25%
Eve	---		
Necklaces	silver plated only		25%
Jasmin	gold plated only		25%
Jessica			
Rings		silver	30%
Julia	gold	silver	20%
Louisa	---	silver	30%
Rose	gold	silver	20%
Stephanie	---		

* 9 carat

Task 4.4

PRAXITELES PUBLIC LIMITED COMPANY

Subsidiary Companies[1]	Operations and Involvement		Country of Registration
	Activity	Allotted Share Capital	
Primary			
Manx (Plastics) Limited	Specialised equipment provider	51% Common	Isle of Man
Praxiteles (South) Limited	Plastic mouldings	100% Ordinary	England
PXT (International) Limited	Cellular telephones	70% Common	Canada
Staff			
Employees' shares	All Praxiteles Companies have established one share owner-ship scheme, and two share option schemes for their employees. The option schemes are savings related exercis-able between 2 and 5 years from grant.		These schemes are basically European. The Americas have separate arrangements.
Related			
Plastics (PXT) Limited	Plastic coatings	100% Ordinary	England
Praxiteles Incorporated[2]	Plastic mouldings	100% Common	United States of America
PXT (Edinburgh) Limited	Plastic stopper caps	30% Ordinary	Scotland

[1] Brief details of principal subsidiaries and related companies with confirmation of group arrangements for employees, including those who worked wholly or mainly outside the United Kingdom and whose remuneration was in excess of £30,000.

[2] A wholly-owned subsidiary.

Task 4.5

STYLISH NEW HOMES AT BRAMPTON PARK

Style	Colour Scheme*		Number Available
	Ground Floor	First Floor	
Detached House			
Kendal	Almond	Lilac	20
Stratford	Mint	Beige	18
Lincoln	White	Lilac	16
Gloucester	Beige	White	15
Bungalow			
Winchester	Beige throughout		14
Carlisle	Grey throughout		12
Canterbury	Mint throughout		10
Semi-detached House			
Telford	Grey	White	8
Chester	Mint	Almond	5
Gainsborough	White	Lilac	2

* Unless otherwise arranged

Brampton Park is the latest Praxihouses development.

The emphasis is on detached houses for young families. Notable features include an attractive, easily maintained garden, generous room sizes, ample power points and lots of storage space. The semi-detached houses are less numerous and built with young couples in mind. These are also spacious and have sensible storage as a standard provision.

Bungalows also feature strongly and are tastefully designed for those wishing to live on one level.

Full details are available in the showhouse.

PREMIER CLASS HOLIDAYS

Departure Airport*	Lakes and Mountains of Italy		Month and Duration
	Hotels	Excursions	
Special			
Gatwick	Grand	Tuesdays and Thursdays - Various	19 May - 22 June 14 nights only
Heathrow	Rosemarie	To be announced twice weekly	20 May - 10 June 7 nights or 14 nights
Luton	Excelsior	Wednesdays	1 - 26 October 10 nights
Celebration Bonus			
Gatwick	Anniversary and Honeymoon Special saving per person on 14 night holidays in selected hotels with special arrangements at hotel, and extra grand mystery tour full of romance!		16 July - 26 August 14 nights (7 nights also available)
Heathrow			1 March - 24 April 14 nights
Manchester			25 April - 6 July 14 nights
Highly Recommended			
Manchester	Palace	Mondays	22 September - 26 October 7 nights

* A reduction will be made for certain journeys if taken by train. Therefore there will be two nights less at the hotel, one each end of the holiday.

Task 4.6

Task 4.7

HOLDERS HOLIDAYS

TOURING CARAVAN SPECIALISTS

Why queue at the airport this year? Bring your caravan to one of our clean, spacious sites and enjoy superb facilities. Our super-markets offer a wide range of goods including newspapers, freshly baked bread and fresh meat. A snack bar and takeaway food service are available 7 days a week. Sports facilities include swimming, badminton and tennis. A laundrette is open 24 hours a day. The licensed clubs will happily cater for children.

Touring Caravan Site	Minimum Stay (Nights)	Available	
		From	To
Lake District			
Ambleside	3	May	September
Appleby	2	April	September
Cockermouth	3	June	August
Kendal	4	April	October
West Country			
Dawlish	4	Closed only at Christmas	
Perranporth	6	Open all year*	
East Anglia			
Aldeburgh	2	March	October
Newmarket	1	March	November
Saffron Walden	2	April	October
Sheringham	3	April	November

* Special Christmas breaks a feature

Caravans are available for hire at very reasonable rates. Please telephone for further details.

PRAXITELES FARM

INTERIM SERVICING AND NUMBERS REPORT

Code Number or Name	Served by		Number Born and Codes Allocated
	1st Service	2nd Service	
Sheep*			
Thirty blue raddle marked carrying singles	Three rams served each group.		Thirty singles, Pen 6B
Twenty red raddle marked carrying twins			Twenty sets of twins, Pen 5R
Twenty green raddle marked carrying multiples			Seven sets of triplets, nine sets of quads, four sets of quins, Pen 4G
Pigs			
0073	Henry	Ronald	Fourteen, NN073
0147	George	Jack	Fifteen, XX147
0318	Ronald	Henry	Eight, RR318
0801	Harold	Richard	Twelve, BB801
0905	Richard	George	Twelve, WW905
Cows			
Buttercup	All served by Bull BB9 (hired from Roundlewhyke Farm)		One, Bp3751
Clover			One, Cr3753
Daisy			One, Dy3752
Dandelion			One, Dn3754
Poppy			One, Py3755

* The main flock had been split into three groups, each served by three different rams. Any ewes not served in group 1 were put into group 2, and so on for group 3.

Task 4.8

PRAXITELES GROUP

A fictitious organisation for examination purposes only

PRAXITELES HOUSE · ADAM STREET · LONDON WC2N 6EZ
TELEPHONE 01 930 5115

REMITTANCE ADVICE

To ..... Jackson, Carlton & Co .....

..... 104 Old Square, PULBOROUGH .....

..... West Sussex   RH10 6EK .....

Date ..... (Date of typing) .....

Cheque enclosed/~~Credit made to your bank~~*
in settlement of the following:

Date	Invoice No.	Amount £
19 November 19--	34856	345.00
1 October 19--	27345	17.25
6 October 19--	27543	11.75
1 December 19--	35100	115.00
10 December 19--	35269	57.50
12 December 19--	35312	23.00
	Total	£ 569.50

*Delete as appropriate

Worked examples

ORDER

To: Regis Supplies Ltd

Terminus Industrial Estate

ALDINGBOURNE

West Sussex

PO23 9PG

PRAXITELES GROUP

PRAXITELES HOUSE · ADAM STREET
LONDON WC2N 6EZ

TELEPHONE 01 930 5115

No: 28821	Date: (Date of typing)

Please supply:

6 reference DG506, card index files

3 reference FL207, magazine files

4 reference DG508, filing cabinets (3 drawers)

1 reference HP405, stand

Deliver to: *Above address/Following address

Praxiteles Group
Branch Office
London Road
CHICHESTER
West Sussex
PO19 2FY

Required by: Ms P Foley	Signed:
	Department: Personnel

*Delete as appropriate

ORDER

To: Williams Commercial Stationers

3 Connaught Square

LONDON

WC2 4EJ

PRAXITELES GROUP

PRAXITELES HOUSE · ADAM STREET
LONDON WC2N 6EZ

TELEPHONE 01 930 5115

No: NG163	Date: (Date of typing)

Please supply:

10 boxes of printed memo forms on continuous listing paper

1,000 printed business cards

50 reams A4 paper 75 g weight

10 reams A4 paper 100 g weight

2 doz loose leaf files

Deliver to: *Above address/Following address

Required by:	Signed:
end of the month	Department: Sales

*Delete as appropriate

PRAXITELES GROUP

A fictitious organisation for examination purposes only

PRAXITELES HOUSE · ADAM STREET · LONDON WC2N 6EZ
TELEPHONE 01 930 5115

Our ref C34/89

Your ref AJ.hf

ENQUIRY

(Date of typing)

To: Office Furniture (Leasing) Ltd
    17 The Forum
    FISHBOURNE
    West Sussex
    PO18 5JE

Dear Sirs

Please let us have, as soon as possible, your best price, terms and conditions for the following:

Details
Supply of 2 executive desks in sapele, vinyl or leather bound, leased over a 3 year term
Supply of 2 secretarial corner units in teak, leased over the same period

Please mark your reply for the attention of ....Mr A Jones.....................................

....

Yours faithfully
PRAXITELES GROUP

Contracts/~~Purchasing~~ Department*

*Delete as appropriate

PRAXITELES GROUP

A fictitious organisation for examination purposes only

PRAXITELES HOUSE · ADAM STREET · LONDON WC2N 6EZ
TELEPHONE 01 930 5115

Our ref

Your ref

ENQUIRY

To: G HENTHORN & CO   (DATE OF TYPING)
         3 THE CAUSEWAY
         SIDCUP
         KENT
         DA4 3BJ

Dear Sirs

Please let us have, as soon as possible, your best price, terms and conditions for the following:

Details
4 EXECUTIVE OFFICE DESKS IN TEAK
BOOKSHELF ATTACHMENTS FOR ABOVE
4 LEATHER SWIVEL CHAIRS WITH HIGH BACKS
4 CREAM FILING CABINETS
2 PLAN FILING CABINETS IN CREAM
2 WOOD AND VINYL CHAIRS

Please mark your reply for the attention of ...MR G GRIMES...

....

Yours faithfully
PRAXITELES GROUP

~~Contracts~~/Purchasing Department*

*Delete as appropriate

PRAXITELES GROUP

A fictitious organisation for examination purposes only

PRAXITELES HOUSE · ADAM STREET · LONDON WC2N 6EZ
TELEPHONE 01 930 5115

QUOTATION

NO .7005................

YOUR REF ..BT/SH..............

DATE ......(Date of typing)....

```
TO   The Headmaster
     Compton Community College
     North Avenue East
     BOGNOR REGIS
     West Sussex
     PO23 8BC
```

In reply to your enquiry dated 1 February 19--
we have pleasure in quoting you the following:

QUANTITY	DESCRIPTION	PRICE
	SPORTSWEAR	
1	Maroon and white football shirt	£15.50
1 pair	White football shorts	£6.95
	SUB-TOTAL	£22.45
	DISCOUNT	£2.45
	TOTAL	£20.00

NOTE(S) There is a further 5% discount on orders over £300.

Prices include/~~do not include~~ postage and packing.

We look forward to receiving your instructions
which will receive our prompt attention.

Task 5.7

Sector: Fitted Kitchens	**Action List**	
Period:.....May....... to....June...............		
Issued to: Staff/~~Supervisor~~/~~Operatives~~*		

Contract ref.	Job details	Person responsible
EJ451	Grey with mahogany trims	J Brown
EM532	All wood farmhouse kitchen	B Roscoe
JY232	Swedish design – units and sink only	G Baker
JY234	Full Swedish design kitchen (replace all appliances)	K Crompton

Supplies to be drawn from stores on Monday mornings only.

Date issued ...(Date of typing)

*Delete as appropriate

Task 5.8

JOB LIST

Week ending ...(Date appropriate to date of typing)

Sheet No. ...2...... of ...2.......

*~~Department~~/~~Sector~~/Division: PRINTING

No.	Job	Required by:
1	3 SECURITY LOCKS TO BE FITTED TO STATIONERY CUPBOARDS	END OF THIS WEEK
2	WINDOW PANE TO BE FITTED IN RECEPTION	IMMEDIATELY
3	CARPET TILE TO BE REPLACED IN RECEPTION	IMMEDIATELY
4	ROUTINE INSPECTION TO BE CARRIED OUT OF ALL ELECTRICAL WIRING	AS SOON AS POSSIBLE
5		
6		

*Delete as appropriate

THE ROYAL SOCIETY OF ARTS
EXAMINATIONS BOARD
SINGLE-SUBJECT EXAMINATIONS

S288
TYPEWRITING SKILLS
STAGE II (INTERMEDIATE)
THURSDAY 9th JUNE 1988

PART 2 (TIME ALLOWED - ONE AND A QUARTER HOURS)

Notes for candidates

1   Please write or type your name and centre number on each piece
of your work.

2   Please assemble your completed work in the order in which it is
presented in this paper and cross through any work which you do
not wish to be marked.

3   Calculators, English Dictionaries and manufacturers' machine
manuals may be used in the examinations.

4   This paper includes Tasks 4, 5, and 6 which form the whole of
Part 2 of the examination.

You must:

1   Complete all three tasks.

2   Use only the stationery provided in your answer book.

3   Insert today's date on the printed form, unless otherwise
instructed.

(Penalties will be incurred if these instructions are not followed)

TSII-2(Summer 1988 -288)

© RSA 1988

TASK 4

(Change 'Turbojet' to TURBO 900 throughout)

ENTER PRAXIMAIL'S PRIZE DRAW AND WIN THIS CAR!

(TYPIST – Leave at least 75 mm (3") for photograph.)

The Turbojet is one of the most ~~outstanding~~ ^{distinctive} luxury cars on the market today. Because you don't see it everywhere, **it** still ~~turns heads,~~

Designed + manufactured with all the care that Turbo put in to their jet planes, ~~this car~~ ^{it} handles beautifully. [The Turbojet has a five-speed gear box, power-assisted steering and front-wheel drive. The height and slope of the driver's seat ~~cushion~~ adjust to suit you exactly. It has gas suspension, tinted windows all round and a ventilation system that filters out dusk/ ^{and pollen}

✓ For the prize we have selected the five-door model. Its ~~fully-lined~~ ^{~~upholstered~~} luggage compartment provides a roomy 21.3 cubic feet; fold down the back seat and you have a ~~roomy~~ ^{massive} 56.5 cubic feet!

Later this year you could be sitting in the cockpit of your very own eight-valve, fuel-injected Turbojet, OR you could be thinking of how you would spend £10,000 cash.

We mustn't forget to mention the stereo radio/ cassette system or the aluminium wheels; nor the economical fuel consumption figures of 37.7 mpg at 56 mph.

Remember, this competition is FREE. You
don't ~~even~~ have to order anything from
our catalogue to be eligible.

Don't delay. Enter today. ← Use any typing
method to emphasise
this line.

Keep all abbreviations

– 4 –

TASK 5

Re-arrange the cars in descending order of price

A comparison of cars for first prize

Keep all abbreviations

MAKE OF CAR AND PRICE*	DETAILS		SPECIAL FEATURES
	MAXIMUM SPEED	FUEL CONSUMPTION	
	mph	mpg	
FORD GRANADA GHIA £10,750	125.45	119.9	Sunroof Anti-lock braking Good luggage space Stereo headphones
TURBO 900 £10,000	125.0	37.7	Front-wheel drive Power steering Ventilation system Tinted windows ~~all round~~
TOYOTA MR2 £10,950	116.0	36.1	Sunshine roof Quick steering Stereo cassette High cornering power

Make style of these blocks the same as the first block C13

* This price is inclusive of road tax, number plates and delivery charges.

TASK 6

Complete the Order Form for Mrs S E Dobinson, who lives at 31 Dove Crescent, ST ALBANS, Herts, SA6 4LM.

She wants the goods to be delivered to Jaxholme, Moor Avenue, DURHAM, DU14 6AX, and NOT her home address. Her reference number is 2151.

She wants to order the following goods urgently and will pay by VISA. Her credit card number is 4929 686 500 191.

1 Organiser Bag, Colour Grey, Item Code 624B, Unit Price £14.99

2 Solar Calculators, Item Code 426C, Unit Price £4.99, Total Value £9.98

1 Leather Wallet, Colour Black, Item Code 828W, Unit Price £9.99, Personalisation details S.E.D.

The order total is £34.96, the handling and delivery charge £2.95 and the grand total of the order is £37.91.

Mrs Dobinson's telephone number is 0727 80810 and her lucky Number is 20202.

Date the form for today.

FORM FOR USE WITH TASK 6

TYPEWRITING SKILLS STAGE II – Summer Series 1988 – 288

Centre Number	YOUR NAMES

O R D E R   F O R M

CUSTOMER'S NAME AND ADDRESS		
Mrs S E Dobinson 31 Dove Crescent ST ALBANS Herts SA6 4LM	CUSTOMER'S REFERENCE NUMBER	
	TELEPHONE NUMBER (in case of queries)	
	CUSTOMER'S LUCKY NUMBER	20202

DELIVERY ADDRESS (if different from above)	HANDLING AND DELIVERY CHARGES (please add to your order total)
	1 item £1.00
	2 items £1.95
	3 or more items £2.95

DESCRIPTION OF GOODS	ITEM CODE	COLOUR	UNIT PRICE	QUANTITY	TOTAL VALUE	PERSONALISATION DETAILS

	TOTAL	
	HANDLING AND DELIVERY CHARGE	
	GRAND TOTAL	

I enclose cheque/postal order, made payable to Praximail Ltd for £

OR

I wish to pay by ACCESS/VISA/DINERS.* My credit card number is given below:

*Please delete as necessary

SIGNED	DATE

FORM FOR USE WITH TASK 6

TYPEWRITING SKILLS STAGE II – Summer Series 1988 – 288

Centre Number	YOUR NAMES

O R D E R   F O R M

CUSTOMER'S NAME AND ADDRESS	CUSTOMER'S REFERENCE NUMBER	
Mrs S E Dobinson 31 Dove Crescent ST ALBANS Herts SA6 4LM	TELEPHONE NUMBER (in case of queries)	
	CUSTOMER'S LUCKY NUMBER	20202

DELIVERY ADDRESS (if different from above)	HANDLING AND DELIVERY CHARGES (please add to your order total) 1 item £1.00 2 items £1.95 3 or more items £2.95

DESCRIPTION OF GOODS	ITEM CODE	COLOUR	UNIT PRICE	QUANTITY	TOTAL VALUE	PERSONALISATION DETAILS
				TOTAL		
				HANDLING AND DELIVERY CHARGE		
				GRAND TOTAL		

I enclose cheque/postal order, made payable to Praximail Ltd for £
OR
I wish to pay by ACCESS/VISA/DINERS.* My credit card number is given below:

*Please delete as necessary

SIGNED	DATE